BEYOND
VALUES AND SYMPTOMS

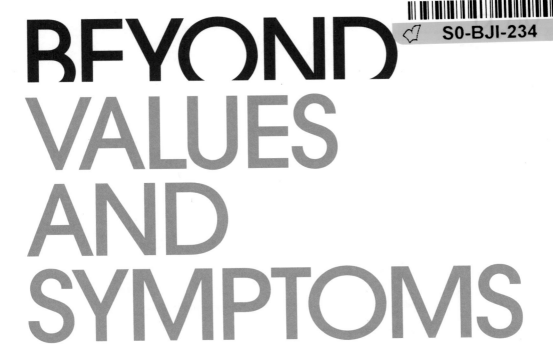

Editor Pedro Gadanho
Translations Paul Hammond, Richard Sadleir
Copy editing Tessa Gerson
Design Florian Mewes
Production Ton van Lierop, Nico Buitendijk, SUN
Printing and binding AD-Druk, Zeist
Publisher Martien de Vletter, SUN

Advisory Board

Marco Brizzi, Ariel Arthur Dunkel, Emiliano Gandolfi, Hans Ibelings, Christiaan Weiler

Editorial research supported by:

Available through:
Idea Books
Nieuwe Herengracht 11
1011 RK Amsterdam
The Netherlands
tel +31 20 6226154
fax +31 20 6209299
idea@ideabooks.nl

SUN

SUN Architecture, based in Amsterdam develops and publishes books on architecture, urban planning and landscape design. www.sunarchitecture.nl

ISBN 978 90 8506 7931

BEYOND NO 2
VALUES AND SYMPTOMS

THE
GOOD

AND EVERYBODY ELSE

THE
BAD

by Pedro Gadanho

"So, what do you talk about when you talk about values?" asked John.

He was freefiing on the lawn, the laptop on his lap.

He started reading aloud from the screen: "These provocative essays take up the questions of what people value in architecture and how changing values influence opinions about it …" He was checking an issue of the Harvard Design Magazine Reader that came on google under 'architectural value'.

The first hit was property crap, but the second hit looked classy.

Beatrice grabbed the Mac from John and read another line from the page: "When it comes to determining the relative quality of architecture, who s best equipped to make the distinctions? Is it the public who lives in and among the buildings? The people who commission and pay for the buildings? Art historians? Or architects themselves?"

As she read on, she was already waving her head. John liked that. He took a mental note.

"Nope. See, I'm not talking about evaluating architecture, or the added value of architecture and all that shit. I'm talking about, y'know, values."

"No, I don't know. I don't suppose you're talking property values." That first hit could still come handy after all.

"Y'know, something that comes before architecture."

"You mean context and all that shit?"

"No, stupid! I mean values, aspirations, ideals …"

"That sounds like fascist crap. Or preacher's crap. Anyways, what would you do with that? I need something I can grab." He made a sneaky smile and took another mental note. Then he heard a passing ringtone and he suddenly got moody. He was missing his Facebook already and he said so.

She returned the Mac. She, too, took a mental note.

"I mean, talk about symptoms and the meaning is crisp clear: you're talking signs and indications. Signs that indicate that, well, something pathological is on its way … But when you're talking values, well, it is not so clear anymore."

One of the few books coming out this year that entails some sort of 'fresh' theoretical approach, Jeremy Till's 'Architecture Depends', looks at how architecture is co-dependent on external forces.

Yes, it is yet another take on the challenges and perils of autonomy within the architecture field. It speaks of contingency, deluded detachment, imperfect ethics, angels with dirty faces and lo-fi architecture.

Which is not bad, since most takes on values within the urban field today are still only concerned with the old fundamentals that rule this specialized culture's understanding of city construction.

But then this has nothing to do with what I want to say here.

What I would like to mention is the apparently innocent fact that Till's introduction takes the form of a short story.

Although not in any kaufmanesque sort, a dialogue takes place in an elevator, in between floors, as a pitch for someone to take in the argument of the book, and eventually buy it.

It just goes to show how architectural writing is indeed in desperate need of bolder forms of pitching itself onto the foreground. One may wonder if it is not the very autonomy of urban writing what is at stake today.

As if everybody's craving for new ways to talk architecture.

Fortunately, the tension can now be released.

Beyond #02 has just hit an airport bookshop near you.

As you may well have heard, two months ago many thousands of Europeans refused to leave the beach resorts of Croacia, Italy, France, and Spain in which they were spending their holydays.

They've decided to riminize, like the tabloids now like to boast.

"We're not coming back!" a raging German from Oberricklingen was telling the evening news team from behind a locked gate in Benidorm.

People do not want to go back to their greyish lives and to their own impending credit crunches. Instead of facing unemployment, they've squatted their holiday premises. They've embraced the better suburb, and the lavish swimming pool architecture of the rivieras. They've embraced the style and the lifestyle of the entertainment resort for good.

"Why would we go back, honey? We're better off here", retorted an angry English secretary from Harpurhey sitting in an occupied hotel in Cannes.

People are simply clinching to hedonism and the ultimate lack of responsibility, commentators have suggested.

Still, it remains unexplained how it all started. There were no organized or connected movements. The idea seems to have flourished spontaneously in the minds of many when the long-standing crisis was announced to aggravate during the Fall.

Sociologists argued that such a prospect had been hiding in the collective's unconscious for long. The eminent Chinese-American geographer

Yi-Fu Tuan has been repeatedly summoned to television networks to explain the inner workings of escapism. Urbanists have advocated that in order to revert this social inclination, cities should now be redone in the fashion of tourism architecture.

A few scholars have also pointed out that the current scenario had already been depicted two decades ago in a little known story by the late J.G. Ballard, "The Largest Theme Park on Earth."

Specialists are now trying to get a better understanding of what the writer meant when he used expressions like "the colonizing of existence" or "deepening boredom interspersed with random acts of violence."

This is the time of remix, of sampling, of anything goes.

Pop will eat itself, as the band from Stourbridge once claimed.

To describe the situation, some will even use fancy highbrow words like hybridization and creolization.

As early as the early eighties, they used to call this post-modern, a term now fallen into the traps of historical revisionism.

However, only in appearance was post-modernism short-lived. One can say that in its deeper overtones it still lures out there, in the disguise of mini-malistic villas next to renaissance shopping malls next to graffiti pa rks next to blobby skyscrapers next to informal settlements next to shiny eco-factories next to theme-parked golf courses, and all of it sponsored by architects and urbanists.

One may be lead to recall Christopher Alexander's 'lack of a shared canon of value', when, in a 2002 letter that is still online, the once renowned architect voiced concerns that the 'postmodern, disemboweled majority of the architectural profession have given up knowledge that there is truth about anything in architecture, in favor of the notion that there are merely attitudes, opinions and disguises, and that each person's disguise or point of view is equally valuable'.

However, in the midst of everything, it still remains to be seen if we should emulate Graham's lament in the red convertible Porsche over the hills of Hollywood. Should we indeed complain of having no one to inform us where to head, what is good and what is bad, like the Bret Easton Ellis character sobs about?

Life can be confusing, yes.

But let's not be moralistic about it.

Welcome the democratic diversity of consumer culture …

"Class.

— verb phrase.

1. Informal. To improve the quality, tone, or status of; add elegance, dignity, style, etc. to:"The new carpet and curtains really class up this room."

2. Informal. Elegance, grace, or dignity, as in dress or behavior: he may be a slob, but his brother has real class."
Definition trouvée via the mainstreamization of pornography.
Beware: architecture too can be pornographic.

One can say that architecture's added value for the urban context has never been so cherished like in the present moment.
If you are hooked onto some of the many news feeds that spit out new buildings on a daily basis, you can only imagine that all is well in the incestuous world of so-called quality architecture and city development.
Even the economical crisis is eventually seen as a tonic destined to stimulate reflection about the quality and creativity with which we contribute towards new urban contexts and a permanent re-urbanization of the existing city.
And yet, here or elsewhere, it is not difficult to find a handful of architects producing some sort of warning.
In 'Toward an Architecture of Humility: On the Value of Experience', for instance, Juhani Pallusma says "the social significance of the art of architecture is now perilously tenuous. Competition over fees, new quasi-rational practices, the imperatives of cost and speed, and, perhaps most insidiously, the obsession with the image are eroding the soil of architecture."
There seems to be some form of schizophrenia going on between the images of a glorious production and the words of the kind prophets of doom.

Think of taste and its classification of the classifier (like Bourdieu used to say).
How far do we go to recognize that this is one of the hidden agendas of architecture today?
Now think of power.
Now think of money.
Now think of …

Many people get high on alcohol, drugs, or power or sex.
I get high on atmosphere. The fleeting vibrancy of a given environment leaves me hanging on an inebriating feeling.
Is this the sort of value for which one can look for when conceiving architecture and the city itself?
Peter Zumthor, master architect, says so.
But how can we cope with the fact that atmosphere is a question of contingencies, a conjunction of circumstances, a matter of a passing moment?
Intrinsically these are qualities that are difficult to insert into the petrifying code of architecture's 'dead language'.

Perhaps what we need is a whole new code for what architecture stands for. And this is not yet properly stated.

Who knows, maybe Feng-Shui will do it.

A visual archeologist from the future looks at jpegs from a long gone illegal housing settlement in the southern shores of Europe. She looks at them with nostalgia. As all spontaneity has been banned from the e-stadt by successive regulation and decree, she almost mourns for the aesthetic loss enclosed in those images. The sanitized landscape around her now radiates a sense of segregation. Was there a time, she wonders, when the euro-fortress seemed like such a moral imperative as to drive people to eliminate all signs of urban dissent?

Are the late modernistic values embodied in the current star-system of architecture – from city branding to icon making, from celebrity design to signature authorship – the defining beacons for the near future?
Talking of 'architecture of hope', let's hope not.
Beyond the experience economy, there is a new notion that deserves a place of itself in the hierarchy of architecture's production of surplus: architectural intelligence.
With any luck the most interesting and upcoming architectural intelligence will come from facing the problems of ever-increasing urban populations across the globe.
As implicit in a story like 'The Dark Side of the Modern', architectural intelligence should rather be springing from the domain of radical community projects, humanitarian ventures and design NGOs.
And this is already becoming visible around us.

Values can be sometimes confused with symptoms.
Like recipes can be wrongly taken for prescriptions.
But Spanish architect Santiago Cirugeda got it right.
All it takes to remedy urban illness is a good prescription.
See also Bert de Muynck's contribution to this bookazine.
When talking role models, architects are the new GPs.
Open a clinic now!

The current issue of Beyond started off with a wild bunch of questions and concerns.

In the face of permanent crisis, what are the symptoms and values that are leading the reshaping of cities and everyday life?

Can we make use of current symptoms to anticipate answers to future problems? Can we employ the idea of crisis to question our deepest assumptions?

Should we rethink our values and devise new principles for action?

As contrasted with fear, schizophrenia, social imbalance, paranoia, greed, narcissism, control, depression, hopelessness, cynicism, and so many other symptoms of the day, where does the post-ideological generation find the groundings on which to rebuild some sort of pragmatic optimism and shared goals for daily life and work?

Uffff!

The answers came forth with amazing diversity, revealing that symptoms can be made highly productive within deviant fictional scenarios, both interrogating a context and generating acute conditions for urban practice – as it is shown in the cadavre exquis that Roche & Sie (n) created for this issue, or in the surrealistic stories by Sam Jacob or Iassen Markov. After Freud we prized schizophrenia, after Woody Allen we treasure paranoia.

As for the old values, it is clear that the quest for an ethics and a new political stance – like the one Roemer van Toorn claims for in the opening essay of this collection – is still dealing with the same classical social and economical foes.

Recalling a recent blog post by Lebbeus Woods and, additionally, a joke about art biennales as the cure for fire struck villages, one could say that what we need now is another utopia.

But do read on and make your own judgment. ∎

PEDRO GADANHO

REALITY DEMANDS

A THEORY

BEGINNING AGAIN

When Georg Lukásc ended his 'Theory of the Novel' with the famous sentence, "The voyage is over, the travel begins"[1] he acknowledged it at a moment of defeat: the voyage of a particular revolutionary experience was over, but the true travel, the work of beginning again, was just starting.

According to the philosopher Alain Badiou,[2] we cannot continue with the experiences of the last century. That is finished.

Rather, it is important to understand that our global condition is in need of a new conceptual framework after the failure of late capitalism and its celebration of deregulation, privatization and destruction of nature.

Instead of solving our problems gradually from managerial, bureaucratic or otherwise apolitical perspectives, we have to imagine the possibility of something else based on a new idea of the common (the collective) that confronts the many privatized forms of struggle in concrete situations today.

With that in mind we should not lapse into older, discredited models of totalitarian, authoritarian governance or return to romantic models of democracy as found in primitive cultures. Instead, we should ask ourselves what could happen now that democracy and the Free Market have fused into a single predatory organism with a thin, constricted imagination that resolves almost entirely around the idea of maximizing profit.

What we need is an ethical project, an ethics of democratic political action within and against the empire of advanced global capitalism.

Now that the current economic crisis acts as late capitalism's moment of truth architects should ask again what it could mean to be modern.

Today, in our society of fear (of the unknown and the foreign) modernization is driven by nostalgia on almost every level,[3] while many of us are absolutely disinterested in the past, in the true history of modern experiments; how architects like the Constructivists, Le Corbusier, Van der Rohe, Team X, Doxiadis, and many others experimented with new conceptual frameworks of the collective and the city as a whole. Although several Modern projects have been disastrous, the Modern project as such is still an unfinished project to be continued.

Embracing nostalgia today – including the modern forms which are taken up without its political or theoretical content – shows that we are living permanently in a form of denial of what modernization does to society as a whole.

Paradoxically, historical imaginations are being created of a past that never existed. Behind neohistorical and provincial façades you find hyper-modern infrastructures of shopping and living.

Instead of creating these 'nostalgias of the future' (as Fredric Jameson once called them) we should ask ourselves the essential question what 'modern' can mean. How could we, as architects, help create conditions of 'situated freedom' for both the collective and the individual, now that globalization is total and neoliberalism has no answers to confront the disasters it created on the level of the city, the landscape and humanity as a whole.

The current economic crisis acts as capitalism's moment of truth: it unveils the ordinary fetishized real structure of society.

Billions of public money are spent today saving the world's free market by those who once advocated that we are no longer in need of a state.

Suddenly the role of public institutions has regained importance. Somehow we all have become 'socialist'.

The bad news is that both the Left and the Right of our twenty-first century have no theory left. Pragmatism has replaced any form of ideological awareness, and especially a much-needed political vision against advanced capitalism. Excavating the real is no longer enough. Merely having all the resources and facts available doesn't mean, of itself, that they produce interesting answers. Intellectuals, artists, architects and other producers of cultural capital can no longer live the permanent myth of rhetorical and aesthetic poetry without being able to relate to the social and political problems of the world. To speak with Michel Foucaul t: we have to defend society more than ever today.

We are in need of new forms of govern-mentality.[4] The addiction to extreme realism, both on the Left and Right, demands that we develop a new theory.

We are in need of a theory that is not only a system of ideas intended to produce reflection, but – as in the Greek meaning of theoria, 'to speculate and contemplate'– is also intended to develop a view and practice of action.

We are in need of a theory that reaches outside the limits and boundaries of accepted fields and methods, hybridizing them, inventing new categories and new modes of experimentation that include the rewriting of history from novel perspectives.

In that sense, theory is also the beginning of the search of the new. It testifies to the need for speculation. And this speculative potential is a space of freedom and invention that travels further than 'just pragmatism' – a space, one should say, that many of us today seem to fear.

What we need is a new theory able to confront the urgent questions of the future, one that develops speculative models and ideas, and asks what it could mean today to be 'modern' within the very domain of praxis.

THEORY FOR REAL

French theoretician Régris Debray has investigated how it is that theories (conceptual frameworks) can end up as world-changing ideologies.

To his astonishment, certain signs, certain words and images get transformed into acts. The parables of Jesus of Nazareth, for example, were reworked by St. Paul into a body of beliefs known as Christianity. The writings of Karl Marx were transformed into a far-reaching political program by Lenin.

"Powerful ideas need intermediaries", says Régris Debray. "I began to realize that these systems of belief – ideologies as we used to call them – are also part and parcel of the material delivery systems by which they are transmitted: if a book like Das Kapital had an influence, it was because the technologies of print, the networks of distribution, and libraries worked together to create a fertile milieu – what I call a 'mediosphere' – for its operation."[5]

From this point of view, the whole discourse of texts, signs and codes (and its theories) are not disembodied pieces of knowledge separate from reality, but are part of what Debray calls the 'black-box' problem. If the input is sounds, words, letters, even photons, and the output is legislation, institutions, police forces, and so on, then inside the black-box there must be what Debray calls 'the act of transmission', a whole set of technologies and environments that translate the input into the output.

Each historical period is governed by major shifts in technologies and how they influence the transmission of ideas. In the Middle Ages the images of God were transmitted by a spiritual class of clerics and prophets through their writings, paintings and religious architecture.

Today, in our visual age, in what Debray calls our 'videosphere',[6] the important fact is not the domination of the group-ideal of one absolute kingdom or empire ('God Told me'), but how each individual can be seduced by a culture of celebrity ('I saw it on TV').

While, with its act of transmission, church architecture played a decisive and influential role – representing God through architecture in the Middle Ages – architecture today mediates abstract ideas by means of lifestyle, brand- and 'starchitecture'.

This egocentric mediation of individual desires, lost in a landscape of splintering urbanism, isolates the individual and ruins the collective.

Therefore, what we need is a political project instituting the common. What we need, according to Antonio Negri and Michael Hardt,[7] is a democracy of the multitude on the basis of what we share and participate in the common.

By the 'common' Negri and Hardt mean, "... first of all, the common wealth of the material world – the air, the water, the fruits of the soil, and all nature's bounty – which in classic European political texts is often claimed to be the inheritance of humanity as a whole, to be shared together. We consider the common also and more significantly [to be] those results of social production that are necessary for social interaction and further production, such as knowledge, languages, codes, information, affects, and so forth."

However, with the blinders of today's dominant advanced capitalism, it is difficult to see the common, even though it is all around us. Neoliberal government policies throughout the world sought in recent decades to privatize the common, making cultural products – for example, information, ideas, and even species of animals and plants – into private property.

The political project of instituting the common within and against global capitalism demands that we develop a new theory of the Modern.

This question of what it means to be Modern can only be addressed when we are aware of the fact that abstract ideas and reality are in a specific and complex manner always interlinked and interdependent on each other. In that sense, theory should be operative; have a passion for the real, make its hands dirty by developing alternative frameworks and should tell the truth to power.

Instead of closing theory departments – as the Faculty of Architecture at the University of Delft (DSD) intends to do in the near future – we have to reinvent what theory and practice research at universities should be about now that the existing political and ideological system has reached its end and is in need of a new beginning. ∎

1   As quoted in: "How to begin from the beginning", Slavoj Žižžek in New Left review, nr. 57, May/June 2009.

2   See interview with Alain Badiou, BBC Hardtalk, www.youtube.com, or New Left Review, nr. 29, "The Communist Hypothesis", January/February, 2008.

3   See Haverleij, by architects Soeters, Van Eldonk.

4   In 2008 we have, at the Berlage Institute, initiated a research on "New Forms of Welfare: new forms of coherence and synthesis that are able to frame private interest within a shared social, political and cultural project for the city" for the policy plan "2009 plus."

5   "Revolution in the Revolution", conversation with Régris Debray by Andrew Joscelyne, Wired Magazine, September 2009.

6   Regris Debray, "Socialism: A Life-Cycle", in: New Left Review, nr. 46, July/August 2007.

7   Michael Hardt and Antonio Negri, The Becoming Prince of the Multitude, 2009.

PAVILION OF THE FUTURE

**"One could not be sure if it was the
work of several architects in
disagreement, or just a crazy one."**

— Primo Levi

Night is falling, and the neon banners on the side of the Pavilion start launching again their bright messages: 'Welcome, Bienvenus, Wilkommen! Welcome to the Pavilion of the Future!'

I've been here for weeks, in one of the lines to enter the Pavilion of the Future. I don't complain, other people have been here for months, like Jamila, or years, as in Dejan's case. By night the Pavilion of the Future is just a huge black box, I guess, lit like a disco jukebox. During the day… during the day, opinions vary. Some people claim they see columns and arches and grandiose chapels. Others refer to the enigmatic high windows, placed smartly so the light beams are targeted on specific inner shrines at special hours. Very post-modern, I have heard it being said, but what do I know? Seen from the sky, it may seem an octopus whose tentacles are made of mangled people. Unfortunately the tentacles do not retract as an appeased cat's claws; instead they grow longer, for more and more people join the lines to enter the Pavilion of the Future.

Yes, most of the time we're stuck, hardly moving, if moving at all. And then, all of a sudden, we have to be on the move. It is quite tiresome, this lack of knowledge – you sit down and, all of a sudden, you're forced to stand up again, only to move a few steps further. At night it's even worse, especially when one is as old as Dejan, or lacks half a leg, like Jamila, beautiful Jamila. Don't get me wrong, I'm not complaining, but they could be a little more considerate. Why couldn't they have built larger doors? Or find a better solution to ease our harsh nights?

"They want people to feel like shit, that's why", sneers Dejan.

"Who?" Jamila asks, as though she doesn't know the answer.

"Those guys who built the Pavilion, who else?"

"You mean the *architects*?"

We actually don't know who built the Pavilion of the Future. Masons and architects, one can guess.

"Not aliens, anyway. Aliens would care more about people." Like all former Yugs, Dejan is a natural born complainer. "These guys hate our guts."

"They do not hate us", pleads Jamila. "Don't say that."

"Architects! People are never good enough to fit in their little plans."

I sigh. I know where Dejan goes. I suspect a former wife – she must have been an architect, or maybe she just fled with one. It's not only the Pavilion, there's an old grudge. And by now I know the tune by heart: architects are disappointed with real people the way fashion designers blame human bodies for looking ridiculous in their outrageous clothes. They forget even anorexic models only manage the miracle for a few seconds, and under the *passerelle* lights. They think we don't deserve them.

I am not afraid that someone from the Security Staff might listen to Dejan's jeremiads, but Jamila is. I wonder how awful it was where she comes from. I wonder how she lost her leg, and I wonder what she had to do to cross the border and arrive here.

I also wonder if I'm falling for her.

Yes, it's not for the meek to stand in line here, at the doors of the Pavilion of the Future, but very few of us give up. Most people brought sleeping bags, and nights tend to be pleasant. And if we're still outside when foul weather comes, I was told the Salvation Army will give blankets to the needy. The problem, says Dejan, is that most blankets are in terrible shape. People who want to do charity should think about the way they do it.

Do not think only poor people stand in line. Here we have all kinds of folk, waiting for their turn to enter the Pavilion of the Future. How many lines are there? I didn't count them – I wonder if I could count them. A landmark of engineering and architecting, the Pavilion of the Future is. Inside (according to prospects I haven't seen but heard about) there are unfathomable wonders of technology, side by side with luxuriant cascades, delightful pools, floating gardens filled with arguably extinct varieties of fauna and flora. And everything is computer-managed, for most of all the Pavilion of the Future is an *intelligent building*, and so cleverly designed everything looks natural and everyone is comfy inside its belly. The Pavilion is a magma, a miasma, a Xanadu where one feels as at home as a newborn cuckoo in its nest. The atmosphere is regulated in order to please each and everyone, it is a revolutionary psycho-pressure device, individual-oriented, even hard cases like Dejan will be unable to complain, for the very moment they say it's too hot the temperature will go down, and whatever their wishes are they will be fulfilled even before being sad out loud. For, yes, this *smart building* can read minds.

"And lick arses. Come on, how gullible can you be?"

Yes, it's Dejan again. OK, Dejan, since you're awake, tell us what you think.

"My guess? They want us in to work as slave hands. Or worse. We may be good enough to build the Pavilion insides, not to enjoy it."

Oh? Indeed?

"Yep. We're like the Indians building the top of early New York skyscrapers. Inexpensive dead meat. And when they don't need us anymore … either we jump or they pull us."

"You're old and mean, Dejan", I say. "Wrong too."

"Oh yeah? Then why doesn't anybody ever come out of the Pavilion? Huh?"

That's true. We never see anybody coming out of the Pavilion of the Future. However, Jamila, always the optimist, has an explanation.

"A tunnel."

"A tunnel?"

"Going all the way to the city, where the visitors are released. But first they must sign a disclaimer assuring they will not tell anyone about what's inside."

Dejan smirks. "So much for the customer's free will!"

"*Not to* spoil the surprise", says Jamila, angrily.

Fact remains, nobody actually knows what's inside the Pavilion of the Future. Dejan says it's slave work – but if so, why don't they let more people in? And why are you, Dejan, waiting in line like the others?

"I'm too old to go anywhere else", that's his answer. "If they Albert Speer me, what do I have to lose?"

"Albert Spear? Spear, like the weapon?"

"I suppose so. I don't know German."

"Oh. It's a German name."

"*Herr* Speer. The secret idol of all architects. He sold his soul to the devil so he could build new wondrous cities over the bones and ashes of *Untermenschen.*"

"Is that so?"

"And later, at Nuremberg, he claimed he was innocent. His goal was grandiose beauty and good taste his only sin."

"Hum."

"And you know what? They bought it. He got away with a slap on the wrist. And maybe they were right. You can't get mad at these people. In a way, they're quite democratic. For them, all *Menschen* are *Untermenschen.*"

"What people?" I ask.

But I already know the answer – architects. Apparently, all this waiting and talking with Dejan is turning my own self into an *intelligent building.*

As for Jamila, she believes the Pavilion will be nothing but Paradise on Earth.

"It welcomes us like a mother does its lost children."

And she goes on: the reason nobody comes out of the building is just that, like the universe, the pavilion's insides are in continuous expansion. Once you bought your ticket, you can stay as long as you want. Maybe forever. There's room for everybody, inside the Pavilion of the Future. It is built to please Mankind, sorry, Humankind, both the masses and the individual in you. Nothing less than Santa Claus giving personalized presents to all the children in the building.

Oh my. I fear Jamila tinkers with some post-communist feelings. I don't mind, given her sad past. Her lost leg. And now I know it's a fact I'm in love with her.

Then comes the worst part: they ask me what do /think. I d-don't know, I mutter, somewhat defensively. I'm no better than all the others, Consuelo, Mariko, Danilo, Bengt, Jamal and thousands and thousands of fellow visitors-to-be whose names I ignore but who share my current fate. And I realize it's not so bad not to know – it makes things sort of interesting, and that balances the boredom of the wait.

Yet they insist. 'Come on, don't be a pussy, tell us'. Well, I say, I don't enjoy speculating. They don't let the prey go. 'Look, don't you know speculating comes from the Latin 'speculu', which means mirror? Of course whatever you say tells us more about you than about the Pavilion. Just play the game'.

I should not be surprised about Dejan's sudden erudition. Still, I can be stubborn too:

"No."

But when Jamila bats her eyelashes, then I'm like a wicked witch–I melt.

"Ok", I say. "It's a showcase of future ways to build cities and save energy in order to deal with the global warming threat."

"Oh, come on!"

I know they feel disappointed. I also know that Jamila is smiling, for I was sort of cute.

And then Dejan stabs his knife.

"We already have one Jamila, all honey and roses and marching bands, little guy. We don't need a clone."

Don't get me wrong. Old Dejan is not a mean person. He loves us, and he knows we love him. It's just that events have a way of hurting you. Waiting too, has a way of hurting you. And I can see that his life was full of both, uninvited events and even less invited boredom. According to Dejan, there is an ongoing struggle between life and death, they're not separate, one after the other, they are side by side, continuously putting pressure on each and both have their fans and their groupies and their armies. The longing to put people in a box, to control and preview life, the longing for structure, is in fact a longing to prevent life. And we, with our imperfect minds in imperfect bodies are in the way of order. Order is a blueprint, and we are the ones who screws up a good plan. Here we'll put up a shrine, there a mall, here a residential tower, there a stadium…

I know where the corollary lies: Dejan hates architects. It's funny, someone who hates architects rooting for entering a brand new high-tech building. Then again, and here I have to agree with him, what's the alternative?

"Plus, I don't hate architects. I just loathe them. They pretend to be like God, they hate us people."

"God doesn't hate us, Dejan!" Yes, Jamila. Who else?

"It might be, but they think otherwise. And they took Him as a role model. Or their idea of Him."

"What idea?"

"Someone who knows better. Someone who knows the way things should be."

"Dejan, are you sure you're not talking about politicians?"

"No. Politicians, at least in the last 70 odd years, have been dealing with the present. There's nothing more blunt and boring than a twenty-first century politician. Corrupt too. Corruption is not such a bad thing, because it is human."

"What?"

"A corrupt fellow doesn't care about perfecting things. Architects, now that's another deal. They believe they can *build* something. They actually think they know the way people should behave. Did I mention Albert Speer? I should maybe add Robespierre. Mr. Le Incorruptible. They don't see us. They look at us and all they see are characters in their tiny, proper, eager fiction. Even if the client is filthy rich. They can't help themselves! And then, when the mold doesn't fit reality, they get disappointed. And they get angry, they get frustrated. But never once they consider that the mold *might* be wrong. Oh no, no, it's the people that are wrong and don't fit in. You complain the window is too high? Well, they claim it is you that are not tall enough."

"You mean we're not tall enough for the people who built the Pavilion of the Future?"

Having made his case, Dejan changes gears into bleak humor: "I'm sorry, I don't think I will say another word without the presence of my freemason."

Apparently (the things you learn when you spend weeks in a line to the Pavilion of the Future), freemasonry was a sort of religion – or non-religion, it's quite confusing – who thought God was some sort of Supreme Architect. An eye that sees all inside some silly triangle, someone with a full view scope. Dejan argues architects take this Superior Being as a role model, instead of Michael Jackson, Madonna or some singing gangster. At the same time they play the modest part (look at me, I'm nothing but a mason) and the not-so-modest part: hey, I'm an architect! I'm the best thing next to being God.

"And they're so full of it. Because they're only tamers, nothing but tamers."

"What do you mean, Dejan?"

Now Dejan goes sci-fi on us:

"What if inside the Pavilion of the Future there's nothing but horror and mayhem?"

"Huh?"

"Not only the ultimate architect, but also a landlord, plus a condominium from hell?"

"What?"

"What if the Pavilion of the Future's architect is not a man but a monster, what if the Pavilion designed itself (that would explain why it is so goddamn smart), what if it is nothing but a devouring machine, and the rest of the gang, the so-called 'architects' and 'managers', aren't but helping hands feeding a giant snake?"

"Come on, Dejan", I say. "Don't be so grumpy. You're scaring Jamila."

"What if we are not the Pavilion customers but its food? Now, that would explain why the lines are so slow."

"How come?"

"Slow digestion."

As to enhance the effect of Dejan's scary words, night falls and the neon banners brighten up: 'Welcome, Bienvenidos, Wilkommen. El Futuro liberta. The Future will set you Free. Zukunft macht Frei'.

The line starts moving. We have to get up. We have to get up and decide if we keep going on or if we leave the line and go away, back to wherever we come from. Maybe without thinking, definitely without thinking, Jamila's fingers touch mine.

And that's enough for me. ∎

FEAST IN A

A PALESTINIAN DIARY

WAR ZONE

**"Things you cannot theorize,
you should tell stories about"**
— Umberto Eco

DAY 1

The firswthat strikes me aboard the El Al plane Brussels – Tel Aviv is the familiar atmosphere. Kids run around and one of them helps the crew with collecting waste. When I look amused and somewhat amazed, a guy who is queuing with me at the toilet says: "Those things you only see in Israel. No formality, things are relaxed."

Welcome to Israel, I thought.

I also thought that this atmosphere might have something to do with the bond of all being Jewish and Israeli going to their cherished homeland – a sort of solidarity and one-family-feeling other nationalities lack.

The arrival was swift. Several people had advised me not to tell the truth, not to say that I was going to a colloquium in the West Bank, for they would interrogate me for hours. That is really against my instinct, the truth is always the best story. But I gave in. I lied well, saying that I wanted to do a pilgrimage to the city where the German Jewish philosopher Walter Benjamin, on whom I had written a book, could have been saved, if only he had taken up the invitation of his friend, Gershom Sholem, the founder of Kabbala studies, who had moved there in the early thirties. The girl looked at me overpowered, just like the one in Brussels who had also already questioned me quite thoroughly before I could start checking in. When I said I would then end in Tel Aviv to see if the rumors on city life and partying were true, she was amused and said, 'Welcome to Israel'. The entire airport seemed run by teenagers.

The Grand Park Hotel in Rammalah looked very posh and corporate and I wondered why the Riwaq Biennale could not give us some cheaper, more cheerful and, if the word is allowed, a more authentic hotel.

On the terrace I met my good friend Alessandro Petti, an Italian architect, who had just published a book on archipelagos and enclaves, with Israel and the Palestinian occupied territories as case study, if not as a laboratory and paradigm for the new spatial order of the twenty-first century. I saw his wife Sandi and Lorenzo Romito, one of the masterminds behind Stalker. This is the rather famous group of Italian architects that intervenes in urban voids in a nomadic way, by non-intervention, through playful, 'ludic' actions, and who enjoy a sort of cult status in the architectural scene. I also shook hands with Khalil Rabah, the artistic curator of the whole thing, whom I never really got to speak to during these days.

During the evening meal we were in a rather awkward restaurant, in a room with tables in a big square, but with really good wine – that was a relief.

Back at the hotel I had a whisky in the lobby with Karel and Ute Lehrer, an American/German town planner teaching in California. So many interesting, charming, excellent people …

DAY 2 CROSSING JERUSALEM

The first morning, we – that is, the group that had gathered on architecture and geopolitics – made a walk through Old Jerusalem. We started at Damascus Gate, which is the most obvious entry into Jerusalem and to me became a sort of grand gateway to this strange new world of the Holy Land – or, should I say, the 'hollow land', like the title of Eyal Weizman's book on the military use of architecture in Israel?

Immediately, we entered a medieval world of souks, shops and busy, narrow streets. Omar Yousef was our guide: a very charming architect in his forties, with grey hair and urbane manners. Being born in Jerusalem, he would try to show us the changes and the encroachment of Israeli settlers upon Palestinian territories. Over a coffee on a terrace he gave us a short introduction with some copied maps.

"The weapons", he said, "are no longer tanks and airplanes, but urban planning."

Before 1993, Jerusalem was central; it was a bridge between Jews and Palestinians. Now it is fragmented. The wall has assassinated the city.

"This is urbanism as warfare", he concluded.

Shortly after, we noticed containers stacked upon the old fabric of the city with Israeli flags on them.

The settlers sort of take the city from the roof. Underneath you see a netting to protect the pedestrians against all the garbage the settlers throw out of the window.

I couldn't believe it. I asked Omar for an explanation. He said: "That's just the way it is. They think Arabs are filth and so they throw garbage at them."

They also try and get houses in all sorts of ways.

The most horrific story is the one I heard from Raed, a young taxi driver. He said that they made young people addicted to crack or heroine till they had lots and lots of debts. Then they said it could be arranged by giving them a room in their house, sort of renting for free. And then they started a sort of guerrilla tactics, making the life of the inhabitants impossible by being loud and rude and walking around naked in the corridors, etc … till the original inhabitants moved out.

Next to a security gate there was an old churchlike structure being completely emptied out, reinforced with concrete and then rebuilt – also a project of Israeli settlers. It is one of the things that struck me throughout the days; how little respect the settlers have for the urban fabric and historical buildings of exactly those cities they claim are holy to them.

What to say about the Wailing Wall? From an urbanist and architectural point of view, it is a triple disaster. The first catastrophe is that they erased an entire neighborhood to make a huge, eerie square, or rather an urban void. Then, there is this completely ugly, shabby, dilapidated, wooden construction that is one of the entrances to the Al-Aqsa Mosque. Or rather, it was because the Israelis declared it too dangerous to be used – but at the same time refused to restore it, or let the Palestinians restore it. To cap it all, when you turn your back to the Wailing Wall, you see oversized, semi-modern, semi-traditional constructions which, from an architectural point of view, are a curse to the eye, but house sacred institutions for the study of the Torah.

Claiming that a place is holy to you, is, I think, not a good idea, but I can understand it. But to destroy the places you claim to be holy to you, I do not. So, I was happy to leave old Jerusalem. If this was a novel, I would say never to set foot in it again. But, as this is more of a journalistic diary, I just whisper: to many happy returns.

We took a bus and had lunch near Damascus Gate, where we met the guide for the afternoon, Shmuel Groag, a radical Israeli architect who, with his organization Bimkom, tries to map and document the systematic urbanist and architectural violations of the Palestinian territories. I liked the guy on the spot. I appreciated his dry humor and phlegmatic attitude. And when I learned soon after that he was married to a Belgian woman, I decided we should become friends.

What to say about the Wall? Apart from being morally appalling, what to say about the wall as architecture? It is not, as Koolhaas said about de Berlin wall, 'heartbreakingly beautiful'. But its presence is so objective, neutral, reified, so … monumental. Indeed, it stretches out beyond the horizon, as 'the continuous monument' of Superstudio or even more like the 'Running fence' of Christo – before he started wrapping buildings, he did valley curtains and running fences that meandered across hilly landscapes, just as the wall does. Comparing the Wall to the avant-garde conceptual megastructures of Land Art is scandalous, obscene. Benjamin, shortly before he died, wrote: "Every document of culture is always also a document of Barbarism." And yet, the reverse is true too, and becomes more so everyday: "Every document of barbarism is always also a monument of culture." Or at least becomes a monument of culture. It is scandalous, but that is how it is.

Think of Auschwitz. My friend Robert Jan van Pelt, who has written three thick volumes on the topic, is right: we should dare to see it as architecture, even as the dark side of architectural modernism.

We went to the gates of an Israeli settlement. We left the car to see more by walking, but it was not easy, at least for me, to decipher the scene. As other cars arrived, Shmuel said: "Yeah, there's quite a bit of political tourism around here." I looked at him and said: "Good word. I will quote you on that." He replied: "Political tourism is important, but it is tourism."

Passing all sorts of settlements, we drove on bypass roads – a tool of urban segregation that becomes more and more important: separate roads for Palestinians and Israelis.

Eyal Weizman drew a famous map of the West Bank, which once and for all made clear that the West Bank is not, like one would think, an unified territory, but is in fact a patchwork of enclaves surrounded, penetrated and cut up by an archipelago of Israeli settlements.

Once you have seen this map, you don't know anymore what people mean when they speak about the two-state-solution. And the most appalling thing is that the real push, almost an explosion, of settlements has happened since the Oslo Accords. Somebody explained: "So, they say they want peace, and in the meantime they grab land. Facts on the ground, you know. Facts on the ground." It is an expression I heard from almost everybody I spoke to. In the vain hope to help and the humble attempt to contribute by coining concepts, I throw in the expressions 'territorial metastasis' and 'urban lobotomy'.

Omar made a statement that would echo throughout the days.

He said he heard somebody summarize the situation in this way: "The Israelis play chess, the Palestinians play ping-pong. That the Israelis play chess means that they move along a very intricate strategy full of stratagems, the Palestinians only react, they only react when they see the bulldozers coming and then of course, it is too late."

Outside, waiting for the car, I met some people.

One Italian Jew, who had moved back to Israel a few years ago, studied philosophy like myself, but considered himself more of a historian of ideas. He was amazed that I introduced myself as a philosopher, but I said: "It is perfect, because nobody takes it seriously." We had a brief conversation in the car while he drove us back to that ever-same Damascus Gate and, as we spoke on Benjamin and Scholem, we both got excited. I hope to see the guy again. One of the recurring sensations during my trip was the clash between meeting a really exceptional amount of wonderful people and facing the terrible, highly depressing context.

A feast in a war zone.

DAY 3 RAMMALAH AND HEBRON

Exactly at six, the group on architecture and geopolitics gathered at the most famous square in Rammalah, the Al Manarah square: a shabby roundabout that marks the centre of the former twin-villages of Rammalah and Bireh, as it is exactly on the frontier of both municipalities.

We started walking the city, past markets, modern constructions that had eaten away an important open space to pass by an inevitable monument: the Muqata, a former British administrative centre and prison, turned into headquarters of the Palestinian authority. Now it also harbored the grave of Yasser Arafat. A big monument consecrates him as father of the nation. What most struck me, apart from being a sort of nondescript emergency architecture, was the huge void full of hastily flattened debris that was in front of it. One day, it could become a square, where the Palestinian nation could gather. Now it was just an vast, eerie urban void – no doubt it was still carrying the traces of the Israeli siege of Arafat's headquarters.

After a walking lunch, we were all escorted towards a bus for yet another, new experience: the city of Hebron. The bus-guide was Nasmi Al Ju'beh, co-director of Riwaq, an erudite, self-conscious, most charming man of the world in his early fifties. He pointed out the settlements to us. Most of them I had seen on the map of Omar the day before, but their physical appearance of standardized, dense architectural ensembles and their presence on the hilltops was depressing. The Palestinian road to Hebron is much longer and slower than the Israeli one. Each time we passed a checkpoint, Nasmi moved to the back and asked a blonde woman to take the guide's seat in the front, so they would think we were all just tourists.

He said if they'd see an Arab face, they would control the entire bus.

It seemed like a vaudeville, but it worked.

In Hebron, we were welcomed by a slim, grayish middle-aged man, who would guide us on behalf of the sister organization of Riwaq, the Hebron Rehabilitation Committee. They also restore Palestinian heritage as a cultural weapon against the Israeli 'settlers'.

We started of in an old palazzo which had very nice details on one of its façades. Via a steep staircase in the courtyard we went to the roof, from where we got a panoramic introduction to the city of Hebron. It is a besieged city. On the hills you see, on three sides, the concrete watch-towers of the Israeli army. They overlook the entire valley.

Then we descended in the old city, the Kasbah, a labyrinth of narrow streets and arched arcades. Most of the buildings were restored by the guide's organization and they had done a beautiful job, at the risk, of course, of turning the city into a tourist image. Yet, there were only a few, poor-looking shops and very few people around. I didn't quite yet understand why, but I soon would. The streets and the arcades were further emptying out as we progressed into the heart of the Kasbah. At some point, we saw a container on a roof with an Israeli flag and underneath again the safety netting full of trash and garbage the colonists threw at the locals, like in Jerusalem. There seems to be method in this madness. At some point, we saw an Israeli patrol passing by. Six or seven soldiers in full battledress, armed with automatic weapons were strolling by. Ute was running after them to take a picture. For some reason this image has remained fixed in my memory – a cinematic sequence I can evoke at will, and one which gives me some satisfaction – as if there was a gesture of revolt in her run, like if she wanted to 'shoot' them (by at least shooting photographs of them). Around a corner, high on a roof, an Israeli soldier looked down on our group and tried to smile, but nobody of us felt like smiling back, for here we saw two streets with shops closed down by military order and blocked off by walls. One Palestinian family still lived beyond that wall, but all others had left.

Luisa Morgantini, our flamboyant European Parliament vice-president, was angry. "Each time I come here, it is worse", she said. "Before, this was full of people, the vibrant heart of the city, full of shops, bustling with activity. They really have killed this city." All of us went silent. When I saw all this, tears came to my eyes.

When I told Alessandro afterwards about it, he was slightly irritated, and while making the Italian gesture uniting the fingers he asked me: "Why is everybody crying over Hebron and nobody is crying when seeing the Wall?"

I admitted he had a point, but I thought it had to do with the landscape, the sort of objective quality of the wall and the subjective, dramatic quality of Hebron. You can see or think, but not feel the oppression when seeing the Wall, in Hebron you cannot but feel it.

On the bus back, I noted: 'urbicide by strangulation'. I always thought of urbicide, the newly coined word for conscious and massive urban destruction, as a military strategy in terms of bombing or bulldozing, but here I was confronted with an entirely different form of urbicide, less visible, less violent but maybe more insidious and cruel. I learned that there are some 4000 soldiers for some 450 colonists – Wikipedia says 700 to 800 – and to protect them they killed off the core of a city of 130.000 people.

We walked back through the Kasbah and came to a strange, triangular open space, with several levels. It was more a clearing than a designed square, for it was destroyed by a bombing. The restoration had left the house foundations, so the big space had all sorts of separate terraces in it and there was even a playground where some children were swinging and climbing. But still it was eerie. It should have been crowded, but now it seemed more like the public space of a ghost town.

At some point, we went through revolving doors made of iron bars, with a constant alarm going off, through a long vault and into yet another one of those revolving security doors. And so we stumbled upon the checkpoint before the tomb of the patriarchs' mosque.

Some Palestinians workers were waiting, silent, subdued and fatalistic, to get their passports back. The Israeli soldiers were getting nervous at our group of over 40 people, especially as our young guide explained the situation in his loud voice. He was saying: "Here you can see and feel the oppression for yourself … But this corridor and this checkpoint are not the end of it. Before entering the mosque there is another checkpoint, and yet another inside the mosque. We have to share the shrine with the Israelis, who claimed a part of it. We tried to restore the building, but they only gave us permission to restore a part of it, as you can see there." This was clearly visible on the building.

People got upset, the young guide and some others started to debate with the soldier, but Nasmi urged us to go. Ahlam explained that if we made a fuss, they would take revenge on the Palestinian workers by making them wait for their ID's even longer. So, the whole group retreated back through the iron revolving doors. Kafkaesque it was.

Later, Ahlam said the soldier was a Palestinian, a Palestinian serving in the Israeli army. She said she never talks to these people.

When we got on the bus, our host, Nasmi, seeing the silence of the group and being a bit struck himself, said: "Let's not be depressed."

As the afternoon was depressing, the night was festive.

It started with the taxi ride. The taxis in Palestine have a robust driving style, they rush up and down, suddenly slowing down each time they arrive at the traffic thresholds placed at regular intervals, only to speed up imme-diately afterwards. So it is a constant back and forth in the rear. And the pollution is palpable.

We got out of taxi, giggling and in the best of spirits.

This evening was the official opening dinner of the Biennale, held in a huge restaurant. Conversation was interrupted by a speech given by Khalil, the artist-architect who was the head curator of the Biennale. He quickly gave the floor to the sponsor of the event, a guy from the Delphina founda-tion. The row of empty clichés he came up with was astounding. We agreed afterwards it was the worst speech on art we ever heard; or, at least, in a long time.

It all added to the artifice of the feast.

Afterwards there was a dance party upstairs in a room leading onto a huge roof terrace. Good music, good whisky-cola, good company. I was one of the last ones to be put in a taxi back to the hotel. I thought again: what a strange combo this is, depressing fieldtrips and exhilarating feasts.

Escape or survival strategy? Maybe it proved the power of heterotopia in crisis situations.

It was during this taxi ride that it first dawned on me that it might be a good idea to give a talk on heterotopia, instead of the one on "Closing the gates: the return of the walled city."

An upbeat improvised speech instead of reading a depressing text.

DAY 4 (OCTOBER 22, 2007)
DEHEISHEH CAMP AND THE PHOENIX PROJECT

The next day – which was a Monday – we went to Bethlehem and the main theme was refugee camps. We drove up in a taxi with Raed and, as usual, he explained all we saw.

At the Bethlehem checkpoint we left the taxi because we had to cross it walking. It was a huge infrastructure. It took us several minutes to cross it. But nobody stopped us – as we were leaving Israeli territory for 'West Bank' territory.

Sandi came to get us in a small white car that had big UN letters on it. We went to ARIJ (Applied Research Institute- Jerusalem), a NGO focusing on spatial policies in occupied territories. Over the welcome coffee Omar asked how Hebron was. I said: "Awful – urbicide by strangulation. That is what it is."

Somebody from the organization gave a concise presentation with facts, maps, photos and figures. She showed a graph indicating that since 1967 the increase in settlements was up, throughout all governments. As this increase is higher than the birth rate, it proved that there was constant immigration to settlements. When she used the expression "Strangulation of the Gaza strip", Omar looked at me.

Then Alessandro explained the new project he and Sandi were developing in collaboration with Eyal Weizman: 'Decolonizing Architecture'.

He started by saying that we know from the history of decolonization that the infrastructure and buildings of the former colonist or occupier after liberation or independence form a sort of dilemma: destruction is not a good option, because you then erase history and have to rebuild from a tabula rasa. Reuse, on the other hand, is not a good option either, because then you tend to repeat history. Often the same buildings that were prisons or headquarters of the old hated regime become the prisons or headquarters of the new one.

Sandy reminded us of the catchphrase of yesterday: "The Israelis are playing chess, the Palestinians are playing ping pong." She said that there is a total lack of planning and planning tradition in Palestine. The notion of public space is non-existent.

We all started brainstorming on the future of a decolonized Psagot settlement.

Somebody came up with the idea of relocating refugees, a school, a university campus.

It quickly became clear to me that most people thought of it as a sort of heterotopia.

Later, we left to go and visit Deheisheh Camp, one of the biggest refugee camps in Bethlehem. When the UN-van and small car were parked, we entered the camp. It had something of a classic scene from a documentary.

Philipp Misselwitz, a young architect working part-time for a Berlin university and for the UNRWA (United Nations Relief Works Agency) was to be our guide. He explained that our visit was meant to correct the vision of the camp as only a miserable heap.

Omar pointed out the iron wires that were sticking out everywhere: they were waiting for the concrete pillars of the next floor. Going up was the only way to expand the houses.

This is something that was also pointed out to me in the favelas of Tijuana some weeks later.

There they called it the wires of hope. [...]

When we finally started to walk on the narrow streets of the camp, meandering down the slope, we were surrounded by children filled with curiosity. Some were saying some English words, others asking our name, shaking hands, others again shooting at us with play guns, some were even throwing firecrackers.

It showed the excitement caused by the visit of some ten foreigners.

After lunch we went down to a sort of hall for performances, rather poor and parochial, with heroic murals on the ceiling celebrating the struggle and the martyrs. Philipp and Sandi gave a presentation on their work in the camps of Bethlehem. Philipp started with saying there are some 50 refugee camps, each with a population ranging from eight to 12.000 people. In the period of the Nakbah, some 800.000 refugees were displaced, now this number has grown to 4.800.000, representing quite a demographic explosion. Initially, two thirds were accommodated in camps; today this is more than one third of the population.

Most building activity in the camps was done from 1967 onwards. The making of the wall has forced further urbanization of the camps. So, more and more, the camps become complete urban structures.

The question Sandi and Philipp started from was: how to develop the camps? It had to be done in close collaboration with the residents, but their resistance was strong. They would say: "We don't need playgrounds, parks and squares. We are a refugee camp and we should not jeopardize our right to return by really settling."

So the work on urbanization of the camp is to work on a changing self-perception. And that is quite different from camp to camp.

"We have to learn from the residents", Omar brought in, "we have to turn the dinosaur methods of big NGO's like the UN into a lizard strategy." And he made a meandering gesture, evoking an escaping lizard.

I couldn't help saying that Omar was not only an architect but also a poet; for he keeps coming up with beautiful, powerful metaphors. We all laughed and I think he enjoyed the compliment.

By the time we finished the discussion it was too late to really walk through more of the Deheisheh camp, which I really regretted. I insisted that I definitely wanted to see Al-Finiq, a cultural centre build by the camp residents themselves. It had been spoken about during the presentation: it was considered a failure from an architectural viewpoint, but the bottom-up initiative was appreciated.

We drove around the camp and came to the hill overlooking the slope of the camp and the surrounding landscape. When we parked our car a crowd was flocking around a big building.

Sandi explained that the Palestinian authority wanted to make a prison here, but the residents had resisted and had finally squatted the ground to make their cultural centre. Nasfi, the director of Al-Finiq, a slim, kind man with a weathered face and big black moustache, showed us the whole place with the humble pride of a master of the house.

Besides a big hall on the ground floor for all sort of events, it had several levels, and one more to come. It had a fitness room with real parquet floor, a theatre hall, a ballet room, class rooms for after-school lessons, offices, an exhibition hall and even rooms for visitors. Next to the building there was a closed garden. We didn't enter it, but from the roof it really looked like a closed garden, an artificial Eden, a claustrum for quiet recollection and meditation. A real paradise garden in the anthropological sense.

The roof was one big terrace giving a panoramic vista of the whole of Bethlehem territory. Nasfi insisted that the roof was an important place too: you could explain to visitors the whole situation, or give receptions and gatherings, or just enjoy the view. I asked Nasfi the big overall questions: why all this, what was at stake for him in this project?

"We had to do something", he said, "we had to give hope to the next generation. Many of us were in prison for several years. I was in prison. But we have to give hope to the young. It is our centre, it is our work, stone by stone this was built by camp residents. We make groups that work for 20 days, after which another group of workers comes. So we supply work. And pride. Everybody wants to help. Everybody is proud of this. It gives hope to the youngsters and it gives them an education, culture and leisure."

I was really impressed by this centre and by their power – and I think also by his power – to create this out of nothing. Never before had I seen the power of heterotopia so clearly. It proved that the theory of heterotopia could apply in extreme situations too, maybe more than in the 'normal situation' of the 'West'.

I said it was very political but in an indirect way.

He was pleased and said: "Yes, this is political work, but in another way."

I congratulated Nasfi on this project.

"But does it not preclude the idea of return by making something for people to settle for, to really settle I mean?"

Here, he looked at me and was firm: "For me that does not change anything. If I could go back, I would go back immediately, on my own. If I would have no place to stay, I would sleep under a tree, no problem. My wife and my children could join me, or stay here, but I would go."

We drove up to the apartment of Alessandro and Sandi in the centre of Beit Sahour, near Bethlehem. They had two floors and a big roof terrace, surrounded by a mosque, a Catholic church, a synagogue and an orthodox church.

"A heterotopia surrounded by heterotopias", Alessandro said with his magic irony and his charming laugh.

Then, it was time to leave for dinner in Rammalah. The Riwaq Biennale had chosen another enchanting spot in a village somewhere, a walking dinner in an old restored palazzo, with a patio and a big open staircase leading to a roof terrace.

DAY 5 (OCTOBER 23, 2007)
'HETEROTOPIA IN PALESTINE' AND OTHER LECTURES

The colloquium was on the second day, and this morning it was our turn: architecture and geopolitics. Alessandro started. He gave a summary of his book, an analysis of the archipelago of control and the enclaves of containment. The occupied territories and the settlements were his main subjects, for which he explained three mechanisms: fragmentation of the territory, connection-disconnection (with the system of checkpoint walls and bypass roads), and suspension, that is, suspension of normality, state of emergency, extra legality. Then it was my turn.

I spoke without any paper or image. To break the official atmosphere, I also announced a change in subject – always nice to catch the attention: "Instead of giving a pessimistic, depressing lecture, I decided to give an uplifting, optimistic talk. About heterotopia. Heterotopia in Palestine."

"What is heterotopia?" I continued. "That is simple: it is a neologism coined by Foucault, designating all places (from topos) that are 'other' (from hetero, like in heterosexual): graveyards, rest houses, saunas, motels, theatres, cinemas, hammans, museums, libraries, honeymoons, holiday camps, etc. According to Foucault they all have one thing in coming: they interrupt the normality of everyday. We, that is Michiel Dehaene, a colleague at Leuven University, and myself, tried to make this inspiring concept more systematic, and came up with our own theory of the three spheres: as heterotopias interrupt the everyday we called them spaces of holiday. That made it more specific, a sphere apart from the private sphere, which is the economical (from household, oikos), and apart from the public sphere, the political (from polis, city)."

Then I explained what we defined as the predominant activity of the heterotopian sphere.

In The Human Condition, Hannah Arendt linked the economic, private sphere with work and labor, and the public, political sphere with action. But she had no real third – only contemplation. I said we had identified the activity of the third sphere as play; play in the large sense of playing theatre, sports, but also rituals, art and study, everything similar to scholè, the free time outside work and action.

Then I tried to develop the theory a bit more, by showing its workings: "What is so compelling for us in this theory is that today these three spheres are blurring. And this blurring, we believe, has perverse effects. The three spheres need a certain autonomy. To keep society's functioning in the balance the cultural, the economical and the political sphere must have a certain autonomy. The intrusions or blurrings have perverse effects. When the KGB, the SS, the CIA, or the police have the right to enter my house or eavesdrop my conversations without a search warrant, it means that the sphere of politics is intruding the private sphere of the oikos. And that is a threshold that should not be crossed. In much the same way, the hetero-topian sphere, the sphere of culture, the time space of the holy, the holiday, should not be economized, as happens in the West, nor politicized, as happened in authoritarian regimes and is happening again now, also in the West. We believe that heterotopia, as a place of otherness, as a place of play, study, etc., can be very important for the polis, the city. So it should be critically defended."

"The three spheres can even eat the others, you could call it the metastasis of a sphere. When politics eats the two other spheres, you have a totalitarian system. When economy eats the other spheres you have a neoliberal system, an experience economy. When heterotopia eats every-thing, you have the society of spectacle, the city as theme park – although the theme park is a fully economized heterotopia, and so it is more of a rampant blurring. Such blurring we should be very aware of these days'.

Finally, I had to conclude: "I think I can prove this potential, this power of heterotopia by giving examples that I have seen on the highly interesting fieldtrips I did during my visit here."

So, what about heterotopia in Palestine?

I gave three and a half examples.

One was the theatre of freedom. I had heard about it from the art people who went to visit Jenin the day before. It tried to heal the traumas of people by letting them make performances. The fact that the guy running the theatre of freedom had been nearly killed three times already maybe proves that he was onto something. But that was my half example, for it sounds impressive, but I had only heard about it and hadn't seen it myself.

"The second", I continued, "is decolonizing architecture. The project Alessandro has just presented is a very clear example of heterotopian urbanism, for both in its content and its form it is heterotopian. The proposals are often centered around a heterotopia: museums, universities, schools, resorts, hospitals. The form of the project is in a sense a 'play', an 'as if', but this exercise in limbo gives space to the imagination, which can feed the political imagination."

"The third example I saw yesterday: the Al Finiq cultural centre in Deheisheh Camp."

And I enthusiastically described the project. I explained that it proved that the people of the camp, especially those who had been in prison, felt the importance of heterotopian spaces: a garden, a library, fitness hall, dance room, theatre, etc. – all heterotopias. It was culture bringing hope to the young generations of the camp.

"And of course, fourth, last but not least", I concluded, "there is the Biennale itself. The energy I feel here, the concentration of excellent, wonderful people, the fieldtrips, the inspiring meetings and exchanges of ideas, the idea of the Biennale not as a temporary spectacle but as a two year process, the work of Riwaq, the feasts at night, make this colloquium a true heterotopia, a time of scholè, of study and feasts, a free time, as an image of a time of freedom.

All this, ladies and gentlemen, convinced me, maybe more than ever, of the power of heterotopia."

During the talks there was noise outside – people shouting slogans. For a second I thought the students were trying to disturb the Biennale, till somebody took the mike to say they were protesting the killing of three youngsters somewhere in the north.

It was a reminder of how close and daily the violence is.

Later, the whole group gathered and we all went in a big bus back to Bethlehem. It took a long time for we had to take the Palestinian road. The first stop was an exhibition of On Kawara. Afterwards, we went to a big, really huge cultural centre, designed by a Finnish architect. The centre was a fine, late-modernist, purist building with all the grace of Scandinavian rationalism with some organicist feel to it.

Everybody liked it. But even if I agreed, I couldn't help feeling a Nordic chill. On the way back, an Israeli soldier came on the bus to control all the passports.

DAY 6 (OCTOBER 24, 2007)
"I DON'T LIKE THE SENSE OF NORMALITY"

In the morning, a workshop was scheduled. 'One city' it was called, indicating – I realized afterwards – the continuity between Rammalah, East Jerusalem and Bethlehem.

We sat in a sort of seminar room, next to a science laboratory or something like that. I remember a vague smell of chemistry. Or was it just a feeling?

At some point, the workshop focused again on 'decolonizing architecture'.

After a very efficient introduction by Alessandro, we were all asked to write down on an orange paper, symbolizing the orange tiles on the roofs of Jewish settlements, our personal proposal for the reuse or re-appropriation of the Psagot settlement. The idea was to just collect the ideas and study them afterwards, but I suggested to quickly ask everybody to read his or her proposal. Alessandro got out his camera and suddenly we transformed into a sort of talking heads, or even news speakers.

There were really very good proposals, encompassing all the extremes of reuse and destruction, housing, campus, hospital, park, museum of colonization and so on and so forth.

Everybody became a utopian urbanist, so to speak.

Or should I say a heterotopian urbanist?

My proposal was called 'the school of freedom', an explicit reference to 'the theatre of freedom' in Jenin, which I had not seen, but heard about. It included a school for creative writing with workshops, writers in residence, an events hall, a translation centre and a publishing house.

The aim was to give the Palestinian people tools to translate the oral history and their traumatic experiences into written tales, novels and history books. In the spirit of an earlier discussion, it was about acquiring cultural power, the power to narrate and, in doing so, literally giving a voice, or in fact rather a pen, to the voiceless.

Later in the afternoon, Albert Heta made a remark that felt like a Molotov cocktail. "I really hate the sense of normality here", he said, "I can't stand it. It is sickening. There should be no normality here."

He was hitting not only at the entire event, but also at their entire lives. One could question whether it is feasible or desirable to be in a state of abnormality for 60 years.

I thought the Palestinian people had proven their resilience by trying to live and even feast and at the same time keeping this very sharp consciousness of the unacceptability of their condition.

Then we all went to the hotel, and we dressed up for a reception and dinner, made by a famous Italian chef and hosted by the Italian embassy. As it was a very corporate building and the atmosphere was too official, I was happy to make a quick tour saying goodbye and thanks to everybody and take the taxi that drove me and another guy living in Belgium to the airport.

The last entry in my black notebook read as follows:

DAY 7

"No real problems during the drive to the airport. That is to say, no problems because my companion followed the advice of the taxi driver not to say we came from Rammalah. When we passed the checkpoint, he looked in his rear window and said with relief: 'If you had said Rammalah, they would have turned my taxi inside out'.

The impression that the entire airport was being run by youngsters was even stronger than upon arriving. All the personnel was really under 25.

After a day of going through e-mails, it is time to look back. If I find the time and the courage, I could try and make these notes into a diary. It could be called 'Heterotopia in Palestine'.

Or maybe better even: 'Feast in a War Zone'. " ∎

A LAND WITHOUT PEOPLE

FOR

A PEOPLE WITHOUT LAND

by Nuno Coelho and Adam Kershaw

The following images and graphics originated on a trip to Palestine in 2006, during which we had the opportunity to explore and research the complex situation in the region. They are part of a book and an exhibition put together under the name of 'A Land Without People for a People Without Land'.

The exhibition was comprised of large format posters, each with a black and white outline illustration. Visitors were invited to colour the posters using the pencils provided, transforming them from simple, impersonal illustrations into colourful and unique site-specific artworks.
A visual discourse was thus generated around the social tensions of daily life in a region where three continents collide.

The images propose a new approach to exploring the Israel-Palestine conflict. The discourse is critical, but it is also ironic, and playfully exposes the absurdity of the current situation. Absurdity is emphasized by the appropriation of infantile language and iconography to illustrate the current socio-political situation as if it were a game or puzzle.

The work forwards our opinion, stating that although there is a global discourse surrounding Palestine, few people can reach beyond the shock images and headlines engineered by the Media and understand the basic principles of the conflict. The work also invites us to question whether it is possible for an artwork to have a political focus without it becoming one-sided or just an act of political activism. Arguably, denying philosophy is in itself a philosophical act, and so perhaps even attempting to create artwork that avoids dealing directly with politics is intrinsically to take a definite political position.

COLOUR IN

THIS IS A PALESTINIAN
REFUGEE CAMP

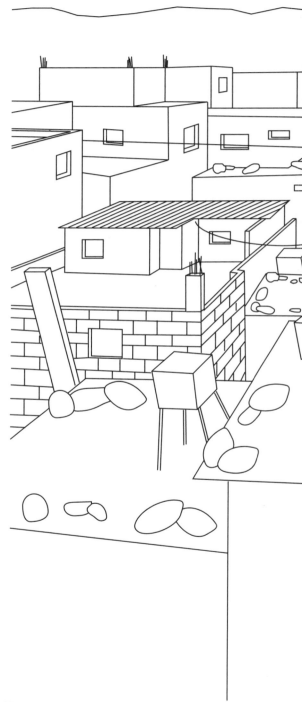

COLOUR IN

THIS IS A PALESTINIAN
REFUGEE CAMP

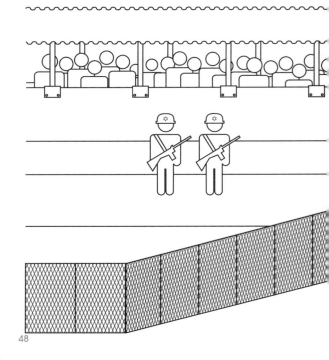

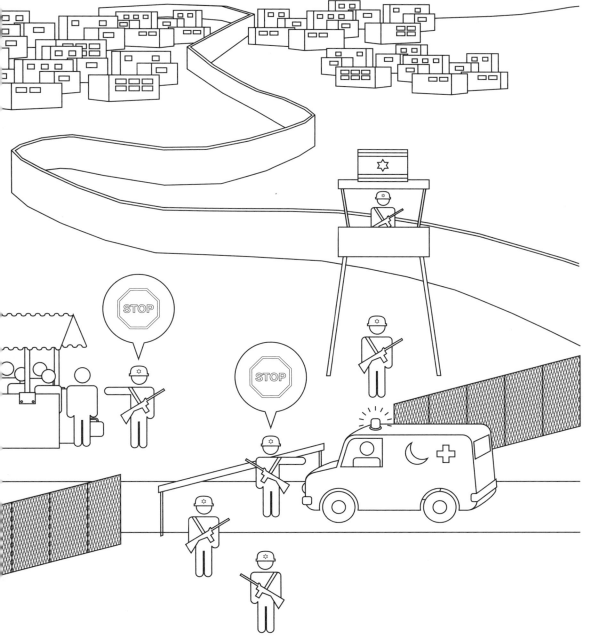

**THIS IS AN ISRAELI SETTLEMENT
IN THE PALESTINIAN TERRITORIES**

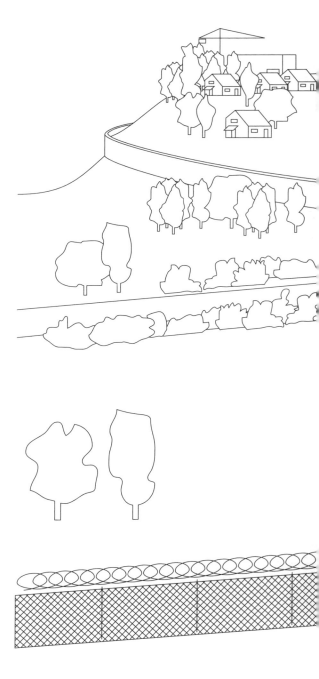

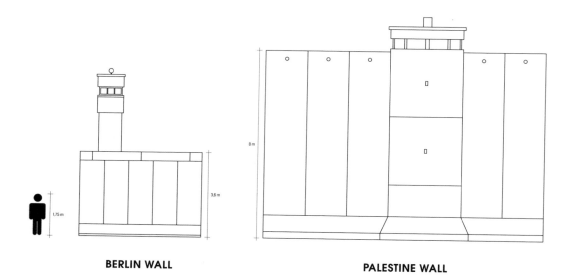

1,75 m

3,6 m

8 m

BERLIN WALL

PALESTINE WALL

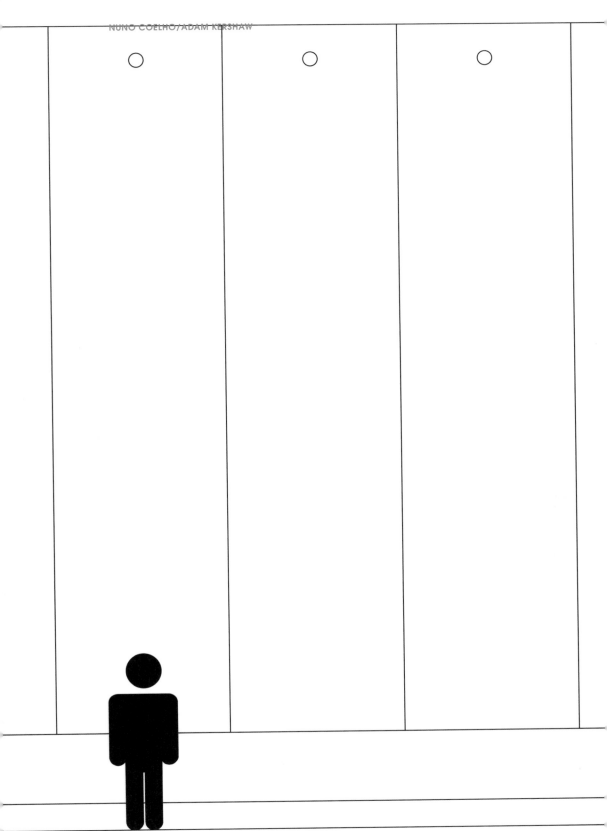

TABLE OF COLOURS
TABELA DE CORES

1 RED VERMELHO
2 YELLOW AMARELO
3 GREEN VERDE
4 BLUE AZUL
5 BROWN CASTANHO
6 BLACK PRETO

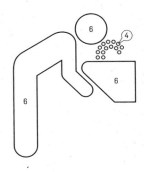

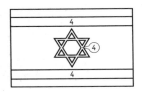

ISRAEL

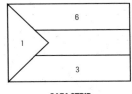

GAZA STRIP
FAIXA DE GAZA

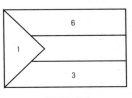

WEST BANK
CISJORDÂNIA

END
LESS
NESS
LESS

9 pictures / apparatuses are used to feed the chat

GIOVANNI CORBELLINI What's this, green monsters?

FRANÇOIS ROCHE Which monsters, did you see monsters?

GIOVANNI I think so but if I look at them a little bit longer they begin to look funny …

ALEXANDRA MIDAL … From the paranoia of the two little girls.
They are about to perform a pro ductive and not at all innocent routine.

BENOIT DURANDIN Never seen that, you mean as a ritual? Like the
reproduction of something on itself, out of its matrix?

ALEXANDRA No, as a little girl myself, I saw them, I saw them humming
"… Sometimes I'd divide / And burn in many places; on the
topmast, / the yards, and the bowsprit, would I flame / distinctly …"[1]

JOKER With this kind of Stargate-like parallel universe, are you sure this is
a book about architecture?

FRANÇOIS Nobody said the contrary.

ALEXANDRA And why not?

GIOVANNI And so paranoia is the key?

FRANÇOIS More than a key, it's an 'apparatus'[2] … In a paranoid sense, an apparatus for submitting and being submitted to a large spectrum of interpretations, from self-illusion to freak three-dimensional effects. We could consider this 'suspended time' as the first apparatus, or, more precisely, how the relationship strategies that are embedded in this 'moment' simultaneously articulate knowledge and are articulated by knowledge. The two little girls are looking at the production of their own paranoia, transforming, at the same time, the representation of our own reality. They articulate fiction and reality, by creating through their subjectivities a narration that renegotiates with tangible substances. We are directly confronted with the boundaries of the system, where, from this scripted confusion, emerges an apparatus which is at the same time revealing the absence of boundaries of self-consciousness …

ALEXANDRA Not so far from the déjà vu: a situation in which you are convinced you're experiencing something you have already experienced before. Buy into the idea of an inexplicable collision between many parallel universes – like Henri Bergson, who dedicated one of the rare pertinent essays to the question with Le Souvenir du présent et la fausse reconnaissance[3] – and you have a weakening of 'the function of reality'. You get a momentary unfolding of the person. No future, no present, no reality? "Pick up the world you can!" could be the White Rabbit motto.

BENOIT It sounds like a Spinozistic motto. "The mind endeavors to conceive only such things which assert its power of activity."[4] It always comes from and leads to experience, as the only thing that we cannot erase: fictions, whatever they are made of. Quantum physicians often explain quanta theories through short stories or fairytales, so as to transpose what they saw onto something else, less astonishing. "Four fishes are swimming in a pool, two floodgates open simultaneously onto two other pools, at the end four fishes are swimming in the two new pools." It's coherent in quantum logic, pertinent in a field of research, and uses cognitive accessibility: the three dimensions required for all scientific knowledge.

JOKER Quantum physics is about ultra-small scale. What happens to sub-atomic particles has not much to do with the actual world in which we live. I hope that the engineer who designed the bridge I pass every morning did it in a very deterministic way …

GIOVANNI Maybe it is better to hope that our universe is one of those where the bridge doesn't collapse … However, the split between classical physics and probabilistic/random subatomic behaviour seems to reproduce itself also in the way we design/transform our environment. And then there is the additional problem that this is no more a matter of scale and that these approaches tend to collide. The continuous request of deterministic certitudes ^{in terms of cost, time, performance, security ...} is dealing more and more with an increasing instability of programs, tasks, opportunities.

ALEXANDRA Who cares about grasping a split between two worlds that even physicists can't explain? Rather, I think it is a start to shift our egocentric and usual viewpoint and start thinking. That is what Flaubert was bringing to the attention, in a cynical fashion, with Le Dictionnaire des idées reçues, in Bouvard et Pécuchet,[5] or, from a naïve standpoint, what Brian Aldiss claims in his novel Cryptozoic.[6]

GIOVANNI You are right. Shifting the viewpoint is our main goal. As designers we dream of the power we fight as citizens. So, the schizoid situation between planning needs and unpredictable developments crossing our contemporary societies is fully embedded in our practice and in our thinking. Hard sciences are intrinsically counterintuitive, ^{our senses tell us that it is the sun that moves around the earth ...} they teach us to set up paradoxical strategies, using chaos to produce open and dynamic orders, looking at self-organization as a possible and more effective (desirable) horizon. But then, we don't have to prove our hypothesis: we just tell stories, and science is a big reservoir where we may fish for powerful devices, tools, arguments, in order to infiltrate the public opinion to build the conditions to make our strategies work ...

BENOIT There can be no more big stories, and small stories cannot be taken as serious or efficient palliative treatments. No strategies are good enough, from an ethical viewpoint, to be immune to distortion. Deleuze-Guattarian theories can be used either by architects or military strategists, in order 'to walk through walls'.[7] Sciences and architecture share the same ambiguous and irrefutable relation to reality. And this relation creates frictions with unexpected results. And it's with those unexpected results that we have to deal, but not as prophets ^{too comfortable}, nor outsiders ^{too reassuring}, nor experts ^{too romantic} ...

FRANÇOIS So, let's take the story about the hermaphrodite polar bears in the archipelago of Svalbard on the North Pole, to the north of Norway.[8] These territories seem apparently virgin, the last place on the earth untouched by global pollution. But it is exactly the contrary. Two toxic streams are polluting its east and west coast: the Arctic stream carries the radioactive substances from the Murmansk Sea and the Russian nuclear submarines cemetery, and the Gulf Stream is a trashcan moving from Florida and Europe to Scandinavia. Confronted with the evolution of these extreme conditions, we assist, live and direct, to the physiological transformation of the Polar Bear, as it becomes a mutant, a Darwinist effect in wild nature. Their hermaphroditism statistically increases their chance of reproduction and survival. The existing five percent of mutant post-polar bears are like characters from Houellebecq novel: brother and sister, parent and children, female and male. By modifying their behaviour and sexuality, they adapt themselves and renegotiate their link to the environment. They are not denying or theatricalizing the global mutation. They absorb and integrate the mutation as a new protocol, as a new contract, as a Sacher-Masoch deal.

JOKER Well, well. Are you sure you want to introduce Sacher-Masoch as a value? Do you want to make a contract with the devil, through Mephisto's servant?

BENOIT You can do as much contractualizations as you want, there is no limit or special restrictions, but duration has to be defined. I would like to choose the territory, a topology that we could all agree on, and a defined area where it could occur. It all resides in where the contract is to be made, not in its terms: all you will remember is the place where you made it, the taste of snowflakes on your tongue or the sweat on your flesh as it comes into contact with the fur. But there is no contract in the usual terms; this should not to be confused with Faust or Sade.

FRANÇOIS The Sacher-Masoch apparatus is previously defined by protocols, it contractualizes and defines relationships which become the frame, the rules of the game being directly dependent on the nature of the contract. But at the same time, the writing of the contract defines the condition of the instruction as a preamble. It seems more contemporary than Faust's deal, where the contract is the definitive agreement to a planification of a no-return. With Sacher-Masoch we are in a reflexive alienation, one which introduces the re-enunciation of the condition of emancipation at each step of its own evolution.

JOKER Please, come on, where is the architecture field in this 'Sturm und Drang' speeches? Do you think you are focusing on something or just digressing from nowhere to nowhere?

FRANÇOIS Well, well, you shot me, nasty Joker. But the 'endlessnessless' is coming from this kind of apparatus, with an adaptable and re-adaptable open source system, both depending on the intrinsic and external mutation of the system. The main question is how we can develop open protocols, able to include wide latitudes of freedom. How can the system develop its own generative evolution so as to react according to the mutation of preliminary parameters? From the early house in the forest project, where the growth of trees was slowly destroying or weakening the house, to the robotic apparatus of "I've heard about", we have always considered the scenario as an open narration where the architecture should be just one element, one shot of time, with a rewind and forward story. And the uncertainty of the system is something we definitively seek, even by crossing to the dark side, by revealing the ambiguities of a given situation. Look at the opposition between the sponge geometry and Miletus' Hippodamos master plan. The opposition is clear: one is an open system, where the algorithm of growing cannot be reduced by a simplified relationship; the other is a closed system, emerging from the architecture field as the very first act of planning, where everything is predictable, forecast, and frozen. The opposition is not only a difference of algorithmic or Euclidian processing. The sponge does not depend from a stochastic equation, but from a kind of cognitive process of induction-deduction, adapting its own growing to its global equilibrium static, photosynthesis .... In this case, the sponge does not deal with mister Sacher-Masoch or Mephisto, but it radically and politically changes the condition of their emission: it could even modify the status of the architect, who, if he follows this profile, will become the alien progeniture of the incest between Villard de Honnecourt and Brunelleschi.

BENOIT This cannot be only understood as a game of 'possibles', even if it has a lot to do with probabilities.

GIOVANNI At school, we were proudly told that Brunelleschi became the first modern architect when he fired the workers of his big dome in Florence. Since he was the only one who knew how to build it, the shared knowledge of the medieval building process was not functioning anymore, and so he could hire again the same men for less money, as an under-skilled workforce. So, modern architecture was born with an act of domination, followed by the increasing complexity of social, economic and technical processes. What is interesting today is that such S&M multifaceted relationship among architects and other social subjects involved in the urban negotiation (developers, politicians, builders, users, citizens …) has become unbelievably complex and fragmented, in a way that vertical control is no more a viable approach. François is right when he underscores that, as architects, we are now playing both the characters of Villard and Filippo. The problem is where and when self-organization and control occur. Indeterminate devices, diagram routines, open-ended scripts and so on are often strategic means to define a set of conditions where we can be still architects, where our specific knowledge does still make sense.

JOKER You sound nostalgic about both Brunelleschi and Villard. But it is evident that there are no sacrifices that will absolve us from the original sin of modern architecture. The knowledge that made us what we are can only unfold completely in fascist situations: and so Dubai and China are now the architects' paradises on earth …

GIOVANNI I'm just saying that our condition is to negotiate architectural choices within indeterminate environments and vice versa. Look for instance at that opposition between the sponge and the grid, where the first is the outcome of a self-organized process and the second a simple act of top-down planning. Are we sure that a sponge-like urban structure is more indeterminate that an orthogonal one? This is not only a matter of representation (organic vs. geometric), nor an issue tied to the design tools we use. A grid (generic) can work as the framework for very indeterminate behaviors, just like a sponge (articulated) can trigger very specific local answers. I think that we should take a fractal point of view, with alternating layers (natural/artificial; Euclidean/non-Euclidean; controlled/self-organized…) that depend on time, scale, two-dimensional/three-dimensional shifts… In other words, to go beyond Villard and Filippo we have to merge them. If the first was inside the process and the second designed the object, we have now to design the process.

FRANÇOIS Many clues are whispering to us, from Architecture without architects by Bernard Rudofsky[9] in 1964, to Frederic Migayrou's analysis[10] of the 'dispute' between Van de Velde and Muthesius in 1914 as an opposition between industrial serialization on the hand and, on the other hand, prototyping as the identification of a situation's uniqueness. This being a debate that has been updated since the eighties, after the two golden bad boys Steve and Bill democratized the toolings of control and narration. Could we consider this genesis period as a frozen one, dreaming of the last retro-future building as a Zaha-homage-vintage-positive-white-future item, pre-designed in the sixties, but strategically constructed half a century after? I know how painful it is to recognize that the future drifted some other way, how it's a lost sensation. We're in a time sandwiched between a predictable future that never happened and, every day, tomorrow's unknown. Something between In the Mood for Love and 2046 by Wong Kar-Wai. The sensation of erotic dystopia, of a charming distress, as a Baudelairian spleen after Walter Benjamin, is a perfect reverse of modernity's blooming, when a lost paradise emerged from the indistinctness between mass production and the production of the mass, when the value of uniqueness' loss opened the way to the overvaluing of repetitions and series, simultaneously disqualifying anomalies or singularities as illness of the system. In opposition, the spleen of today does not stem from the loss of value, but from the impossibility to attribute value to this uniqueness, definitively lost after the experience of the afterdeath of modernity. How can we take refuge within this condition, somewhere in a comfortable back room? The conditions of today, here and now, are palpitating between dream time and day after, as altered states mix with schizoid ingredients, with a pinch of Clockwork Orange (with its CIA-designed torture scene) and another one from 2001: A Space Odyssey (with its NASA-designed Galilean escape).[11] It seems difficult to simplify this reality, to reduce it to a simple univocal game, without considering the ensemble of heterogenic tooling integrating speeches, regulations, strategies, scientific protocols, games of power and stories of self-alienation, integrating talks, non-talks and misunderstandings such as the network, the rhizome of narrative, the scenario … And these appear as preliminary enunciations of the apparatus of an architectural item, where the apparatus cannot be itself reduced to the definition of the architectural part, Situationist strategies,[12] where the input and output became contingents, where ambiguities are articulated between themselves, where the protocol of transformation reveals the condition of their emission…

ALEXANDRA I'd like to go back to the famous 1914 acrimonious polemics between Muthesius and Van de Velde. Far from giving the standard romantic analysis, the co-founder of the Deutscher Werkbund was indeed more of an idealist than Van de Velde. According to Frederic Schwarz, the most important fact of the debate consisted in the emergence of the copyright notion, and of the artist, architect, and designer as the legal equivalent of the industrial. The controversy indicates a primary discussion about mass culture and mass-media culture, as it is published and exhibited before an audience. While identifying the contemporary attraction for the future attached to the sixties through formalist derivation, the reduction of the future can be considered simply as an aesthetic decision reflecting the taste of the author, its uniqueness. But from the point of view of futuristic content, the intensity of revisiting fiction, or the blooming dystopias, such fascination seems to flirt only with commercial business. Is there no exit? No. The future is gone, as Ballard claims,[13] as well as the technological potential embodiment attached to it. I don't think there is any legitimate space left for refuge.

BENOIT Yes or no, the future is gone and will never be. Climatologists are the first ones to acknowledge that they will never be able to make accurate predictions even about mid-term developments, and even if one day they own computers as fast as the demon of Laplace. Actually, they prepare themselves to the uncertainty issues of climatic changes by elaborating families of scenarios. Those scenarios deal with hierarchies, but more interesting with heterarchies of information.

FRANÇOIS Our digression revolves around our subject, as a very carefully approach, with no cadavers in the cabinet. The speeches seem to be on a very strategic point. As we said, 'endlessnessless' is a tooling for narration, for uniqueness, not for emphasis of industrialization or repetition. It includes and produces scenarios of singularity, of anomaly. 'Endlessnessless' redefines the 'Aura' of items. In a way, this narrative machine, which is physically extracted, screw by screw, from the mass industrialization, is able to escape from this genesis and also to develop both stories and reality principles, application scripts, constructive behaviors and impermanency, uncertainties. This kind of post-bachelor machine comes from the incest between the

T1000 and Picabia's Ghost[14] and introduces subjectivities in the touchable substances of physical transformation. This is one of the ambiguities, even if not the main one: at the middle of these huge prototyping possibilities, we are paradoxically infiltrated by a spleen, confronted to the difficulties to apply or define value to this uniqueness we can now realize. This works as the lost sensation described by Baudelaire,[15] but in a perfect symmetric direction; as kids of Tron[16] (computer nerds swallowed by the software), we are technologically able to realize a rare and unique prototype, but the primary reason of this prototyping product has been digested by a Miyazaki[17] monster and lost within the system of massification of desire. It's a very strange state that, at the time we can be involved with computational design, with a non-standard approach, the intrinsic senses and values of this approach and production drift and shift somewhere, like in a magnetic black hole …

JOKER This seems to be a pre-romantic discussion, just like the Goethian Sturm und Drang-movement stood against the rationalism of Enlightenment and the positive outlook of the Encyclopedia. But architecture has always been proposed with this kind of positive aims and purposes, as a vector of progressive projection. Are you, in opposition, regressively and pathologically alienated by the Faustian deal?

BENOIT Recent researches in biology push us to think that there is no 'intelligence' other than a silly one.[18] If you put bees and flies in a bottle couched on the ground, the bees will die after a few hours exhausted by bumping against the glass, as their instinct tells them to go where they see light; on the other hand, flies will find their way out sooner or later by the neck of the bottle: their apparently erratic and uncoordinated manner of flying being much more efficient. But even if we can determine the causes, such understanding leads to no real knowledge and comprehension. If systemized, knowledge and its applications cannot be replicated. Pierre Gourou, a French geographer, went to what is now Vietnam[19] in 1927 to understand why the density of population was so high. Looking at countries situated at the same tropical latitude and with the same kind of agricultural exploitation, such density was totally anomalous. The population of the country should have been much lower. He discovered and proved that it was 'culture' and the 'society' that allowed the population to grow in this unexpected manner. It was not due to a system, nor a special technology. And, most importantly, this could not be reproduced, even in similar countries situated under the same tropical latitude. What we today call externalities created the conditions for this unpredictable human growth. But the difficulty to calculate and to know precisely their role, made that externalities were hardly integrated into any soft or hard practices. What we call noise is completely transforming our understanding of physics and social phenomena.

GIOVANNI I think we can agree that to design means to deal with cause-effect relationships. It may sound an enlightenment or positivist statement, but it is a condition that is very hard to escape. On the other hand, we know that deterministic actions are less and less likely to get the effects they expected. There is a joke about TV ads in Italy that reflects this: some years ago, a spirits firm promoted its product with the adventures of a veterinarian. They didn't sell one more bottle, but the veterinary faculties had a lot of new students … The majority of architects tried and tries to resist this situation, since they feel all this indeterminacy as a deadly threat to the core business of the discipline, i.e. authorship and formal control over the built outcomes. But reality escaped them and the occasions where the architect can actually control building processes are falling down. And so, one of Volume's latest issues shows that even celebrity doesn't assure the final cut. As a result, the last 25 years architectural avant-gardes moved their struggle against the establishment from the language field to an operative one, dealing with indeterminate processes, bottom-up techniques, open-ended devices, interactive protocols … They triggered a conceptual shift that brought proliferation – rather than composition – to the foreground. But proliferation alone is not so clever. It is an accelerating tool, like the gamma rays used to get mutations in the wheat seeds. They do have to sow them and breed some generations to understand which are the fittest. One of the weaknesses of the 'non-standard'[20] approach (especially in America) resides in its lack of direction or, in other words, in its search of novelty as an absolute value. It seems that many outcomes are simple consequences of technological possibilities: answers in search of a question. They act as gamma rays (or the flies in the bottle), producing a large amount of alternative solutions waiting for something (critics, magazines, market, clients …?) to select the next architectural 'real thing'. This is not so different from what happens in the turbo-capitalistic development of the eastern tigers: I've heard that in Bangkok they thought about building two different metro lines to serve the same area, waiting to see which one would survive …

BENOIT For sure, we are now in the realm of cognitive capitalism, where all the fields of what is 'free' time or 'free' production are reabsorbed and instrumentalized to justify positions and roles, or to nourish contingencies. But refusing to empower any direct cause-effect relationship for a while – to consider them as something purely illusory, only made to feed hollow simulacra and replicas – helps us to avoid such instrumentalizations. We, at R&Sie(n), take the singularities as the main subject in our architectural practice, as the most fertile ground. No more a pure arrow of cause-effect, but a succession of frozen objects, in different states, loaded with all the 'affects' that they went through. This approach has the advantage to not let us sink into a world only ruled by probabilities. There is this fascinating Philip K. Dick book,[21] Solar lottery, where the story takes place in a world entirely controlled by probabilities, a world in which "the causality concept is disappearing from the human thought." The most interesting part about this world was how human minds were able to create machines that were calculating those probabilities, and how human minds then face the uncertainty produced by those machines – and cheat with it of course, as we are in the paranoid world of P. K. Dick. Those two metro lines in Bangkok make me think about the 1936 non-determinist machine by Alan Turing, which allows several results for the same calculation: negative, positive or indeterminate, all of them being 'non-untrue'.

FRANÇOIS I remember the voice of Antonin Artaud in the borderline radio play Pour en finir avec le jugement de Dieu, registered just after the Second War World and forbidden during 40 years.[22]
Screaming, whispering, crying, he was vomiting about how les 'americains fabriquent des machines et sont fabriqués par celles-ci'. I understand deeply this machinist claim at a period where Cybernetics and Artificial Intelligence were developed as ideology. Instead, the bachelor machine or apparatus articulated by R&Sie(n) are borrowing the possibility of machinism as a protocol for subjectivities. They are borrowing tools coming from scientific, technical and technological backgrounds, so that from them emerges a kind of indeterminacy and, by this, the failure of their positive nature and their structural logic may be instrumentalized. There are always ghosts intrinsically hidden within and beyond science practices …

BENOIT Some of our friends, by refusing any retro- or techno-future, want to live in an illusory and perfect suitability to the present time. It leads them to believe in the precision, the efficiency and the honesty of the tools that they have access to. Even if we can't consider it as plain positivism, it leads to a sort of scientific mysticism, understandable by what it tries to avoid, but not by what it generates. Ballard declared in 1962 that "the only truly alien planet is Earth."[23] The literary approach known as speculative fiction never worked on a perfect timeline. There is always subtle shifts, small gaps within reality that allow fiction to enter, to create the openings, to be an instrument of transformation. Pure computational determinisms, on the other hand, preserve their authors from this risk, it allows them to refuse speculation because of the impossibility to have full control of it. But speculation is a dynamic and physical object, it's always in motion, it's subject to the Doppler effect: it's by its taste and color that you can recognize and understand its shifting.

ALEXANDRA I am back with the bachelor machines. The sexual frustration attached to the machines provides a line of thought which starts with Villiers de l'Isle-Adam's L'Ève future[24] and finds a new stance in R&Sie(n)'s dystopia zone machines. Let's go back to one of its sources: Raymond Roussel's Locus Solus or Impressions d'Afrique's texts[25] played in 1912 at the Théâtre Antoine, in Paris, at the sole expense of the rich and eccentric French writer. The whole avant-garde, from Duchamp to Breton, attended the show and, as they were stunned by its various artifacts, it is no surprise that the sexual nature of technology became such a paradigm in their respective works. It constructs an interpretation of a machine symbolizing a pure bliss through both onanism and a sexual liberating and non-repressive sadomasochist pact. The whole range of the bachelor machines, including Duchamp's Bride Stripped Bare by her Bachelors, Even masterpiece, borrow from the coitus-interruptus process. As they prevent the deposit of sperm into the vagina and therefore focus on bliss and reject production, the idea of pure pleasure lies at their heart. Bachelor machines don't give a damn about cloning or duplication … they crave for pleasure, and only pleasure! And such legacy is necessary to fulfill the R & Sie(n) machines. Orgasm is achieved through the power of the mind – or subconsciously. As Deleuze puts it, "the subconscious is a factory, a machine for production", and here arises a genealogy of sluggish and desiring machines and machinations from Duchamp to R & Sie(n).

FRANÇOIS In the scenario of R & Sie(n), the 'bachelor apparatus' has to be assimilated to a vector of narration, like the Lyre of Orpheus, going down in the kingdom of Hades to bring back his sweetheart, Eurydice, and playing music to bewitch the wild animals and the devil as he goes along. At the same time, the apparatus creates an operative effect and a blurring logic. The apparatus builds ambivalences, both by narrative and procedural mode… as schizoid contingencies … and the machine becomes the vector of a constructive subjectification.

To tell a story about architecture, R&Sie(n) introduces its own MacGuffins. As in Hitchcock, there are clues from which the story can unfold, but soon the movie releases itself from this origin and, after a time, becomes independent of the initial clue. The Olzweg machine, made for FRAC, is the starting point of indeterminacy, of random behaviour and of the process of loosing control so as to define an unpredictable shape. The endlessness needs this clue, which is both narrative and operative, to create the condition of a further step, of an un-achievement, of an 'After Death Experience' appearing as a prolongation of the construction. For this, R&Sie(n) apparatuses are using stochastic machines, psycho-machines, chimera robots, speculative mechanics, anthroposophic systems, de-polluting processes, environmentalist ecosophic devices, paranoid artificial climates for negotiating our fears of transforming biotopes… The machine protocols, on the other hand, are psycho-masomachinisms that include misunderstanding, 'des malentendus', and frustrations. The level of freedom, the latitude of randomization of the behaviour, is developed as a corruption of the application – as it happens with stress input, in the case of 'I've heard about'. The script, the algorithm that drives the machine, is disrupted by internal agents dealing with 'if, then' and 'while' possibilities and alternatives. But, as

I mentioned, the main aspect of the apparatus is to reveal, to release the contradictions of a situation. They are not simplifying and denying the preliminary complexities, but they define a strategy of mutation directly extracted from their recognition.

Are they desirable and desiring, in a sense of the Body without Organ, defined by Artaud and Guattari?[26] I hope so … Their eroticization, their sexualization, weeps from the context where they are embedded, within the rhizome, at the exact opposite of a panoptical unfolding. As the sentence of Pessoa in 1952 – "I'm coming from before the reality"[27] – the apparatus place the body of architecture in a space that is combining reality and the real, using fiction as traveling vehicle.

JOKER Are you playing music, as the endless Titanic song?

FRANÇOIS The nature of the music during the sinking of the Titanic is still an object of debate. Some survivors heard "Nearer, my God to thee" and some others "Alexander's Ragtime Band." Why did the witnesses' memories hesitate between the ideal request of the God-song and profane ragtime, as if divided between the deal of death and the ultimate human rage against the deal? If you want to compare, dear Joker, R & Sie(n) is improvising both simultaneously. But don't confuse yourself, the Lyre instrument is only a decoy, a lure. It assumes the operative and visible part of the apparatus composed by a more sophisticated cooking with a pinch of an Ecosophy empathy as the recognition of a preliminary situation,[28] a pinch of a Sacher-Masoch contract as a rule of the game or scenario,[29] a pinch of an Anthroposophic loop as an exchange of substances,[30] a pinch of an heterotopian[31] sensation as a protocol of indeterminacy and stochastic behaviour, and lastly, as the cherry on the cake, a pinch of a dynamic agent or Lyre, to operate the story, as from Orpheus' hands.

JOKER Yes, yes, you got it … ! The five points? Again? As a revival of the night of the zombies?

FRANÇOIS You killed me my friend.
"I'm late, I'm late, I'm late!" said the White Rabbit.
It is time for Alice to jump into her parallel universe.
Like her, now, we could confuse our own paranoia with the unreality of our perception.

Endless. ∎

1   William Shakespeare, The Tempest, 1611, Ariel, Act 1, sc 2, 195–200

2   See Giorgio Agamben, Che cos'è un dispositivo, Nottetempo, 2006

3   Henri Bergson, 'Le Souvenir du present et la fausse reconnaissance', in Revue philosophique, Dec. 1908, pp 561–593. English translation in Mind-Energy. Macmillan, 1920

4   Baruch Spinoza, Ethica ordine geometrico demonstrata, 1661–77, parte III, prop. 54

5   Gustave Flaubert begins Bouvard et Pécuchet in 1872. It is published unfinished in 1881.

6   Brian Aldiss, Cryptozoic, Faber, London 1967

7   See Eyal Weizman, 'Lethal Theory', Log, n. 7, 2006

8   See, for instance, David Usborne, 'Toxic Waste Creates Hermaphrodite Arctic Polar Bears', in The Independent, January 10, 2006

9   Bernard Rudofsky, Architecture without architects. An introduction to nonpedigreed architecture, Moma-Doubleday, 1964

10 Frederic Migayrou in Architecture Non Standard, exhibition catalogue, Centre Pompidou, 2004

11 Both movies were notoriously directed by Stanley Kubrick, whose first feature film was Fear and Desire, 1953, with a team of soldiers trapped behind enemy lines in a fictional war.

12 Guy Debord, La société du spectacle, Buchet/Chastel, 1967; Constant and Guy Debord, La déclaration d'Amsterdam, in 'Internationale situationniste', n. 2, December 1958, pp. 31–32

13 James G. Ballard, 'Back to the Heady Future', in The Daily Telegraph, April 17, 1993.

14 See 'Máquinas y españolas' exhibition at the Galeries Dalmau, Barcelona, in 1922.

15 'Perte d'Auréole' or 'Loss of a Halo', Charles Beaudelaire, Le Spleen de Paris, 1864.

16 Movie by Steven Lisberger, 1982.

17 The black digestive intestine in the movie of Hayao Miyazaki, Sen to Chihiro no Kamikakushi (Spirited Away), 2002.

18 Mathieu Aury, 'Darwin révolutionnaire? Une lecture politique de Dennett', in Multitudes, n. 16, 2004, Philosophie de la biologie. English readers could read Daniel C. Dennet, Darwin's Dangerous Idea. Evolution and the Meanings of Life, Simon & Schuster, 1995.

19 Pierre Gourou, Les paysans du delta tonkinois, 1936. See Jacques Lévy and Michel Lussault, Dictionnaire de la géographie I, Belin, 2003, entry 'Pierre Gourou'.

20 See 'Non-Standard Architecture' exhibition, Centre Pompidou, Paris, curated by Frédéric Migayrou and Zeynep Mennan.

21 Solar Lottery, Ace, 1955.

22 Antonin Artaud, Pour en finir avec le jugement de dieu, French National Radio, Paris. November 1947.

23 J.G. Ballard, 'Which Way to Inner Space', in New Worlds, 1962.

24 Auguste de Villiers de L'Isle-Adam, L'Ève future, 1886.

25 Impressions d'Afrique, 1910, and Locus Solus, 1914, by Roussel are part of the bachelors machines corpus delineated by Michel Carrouges or Harald Szeeman etc.

26 Corps Sans Organe, or CsO, is a concept developed by Deleuze and Guattari in Mille Plateaux and Anti-Oedipe, after Artaud: 'Il n'y a rien de plus inutile qu'un organe. Lorsque vous lui aurez fait un corps sans organes, alors, vous l'aurez délivré de tous les automatismes et rendu à sa véritable et immortelle liberté'.

27 Fernando Pessoa, Anarchism, in Magazine Littéraire, n. 291, September 1991, p. 29.

28 Felix Guattari, Les trois ecologies, Paris, Gallilée, 1989.

29 Rudolph Steiner, Les lignes directrices de l'anthroposophie, 1924.

30 Gilles Deleuze, Michel Foucault. Le Cruel et le Froid. Presentation de Sacher Masoch, Ed. de Minuit, 1967

31 Michel Foucault, Utopie et Heterotopie, lecture for National French Radio, 1966.

EVERY THING DALE MYERS COULD AND COULDN'T SEE

Myers pulled into the parking lot of an industrial unit that was home to his digital animation studio. The early morning sun reflected on the ribs of its corrugated steel cladding.

Inside, he started up his workstation, the screen illuminating like an artificial dawn. Its cool white light shone onto his face, radiating a sense of undisturbed calmness. Myers felt close to another world, gazing through the screen into somewhere that had complete clarity. There, he knew the position of every object. Every quality that the world contained was listed, its entire history logged in an undoable list.

This absence of doubt was so very different from the confusion Myers felt when he looked away from the screen. Across the studio, there were wires that led to places no one could remember. Half filled boxes might be rubbish or important archives. So much vagueness, so much that was unresolved and unknowable.

Myers worked on animating characters. Some of them you've probably seen. His was the work that brought M&Ms to life for commercials. Myers would be briefed by advertising creatives, shown sketches, talked through characterization. He would take notes as twenty-something hipsters loped around the room in an effort to demonstrate the kind of exaggerated spongy gait they wanted him to create. They gave him a binder of sketches showing Ellipsoid primary colored shapes spouting bits of biology: arms, legs, eyes, mouth. They gave him dialogue that anthropomorphized these candy-creatures into wisecracking buddies. Already, Myers imagined wire frame geometries – the mathematical armatures onto which all this characteri-zation would be projected. Angles, rotations, and formula describing arcs of movement filled his mind, gone glowing white as the space of a virgin virtual world.

Myers' success began with Squeaky and Lumpy, animated characters devised for a Virginia based firm called Grand Home Furnishings. Shortly after this he produced Robo Jr, the story of a curious young robot who takes the family flying saucer for a joyride. It won four Emmys, and since then Myers' animation studio had gone from strength to strength. They now occupied a large swathe of an industrial estate, three highly serviced sheds occupied by computer suites, motion capture studios, three-dimensional scanners and rapid prototype machines.

But the project that really occupied Myers' mind was located toward the back of the third of these sheds. This was a project he had begun back in the early nineties on an Amiga 2000 computer with a 286 processor attached to a NewTek Video Toaster with a 24-bit display card.

Using Lightwave, Myers had been constructing a model of the assassination of President Kennedy. He began to collect data and documents, feeding the information into his model: the geography of Dealey Plaza, the positions of the waving crowds, the architecture of the Book Depository, the position and size of trees began to be mapped out.

Myers assembled a growing library of documents, maps, newspaper reports, eyewitness accounts and photographs, triangulating between them to pinpoint positions, double check measurements, map out the sequence of events.

As Myers worked through his project he felt a sense of abstract stillness leaking out from his screen. Myers' idea was that something of the clarity of his mathematically described environments might be able to be mapped onto the landscape of the real world. That somewhere where the direct relationship between action and reaction, between intention and effect was immediate, it might be able to point to a place and a moment that seemed to represent the degree zero of the unresolved and unknowable. Through this, a non-negotiable truth might emerge.

During the nights after animating red and yellow M&Ms, he made notes charting the Zapruder assassination footage frame by frame:

Frame 313/161.2 grain slug, traveling at 2,100 ft/sec. Hits R. occipital area of Kennedy's head, shattering occipital bone. Upper R side of head explodes, brains/bone in expanding pink cloud. Pieces of parietal and temporal sections skull remain attached by skin. Head lurches back to the left (8.0–8.4 seconds after the first shot). Body stiffens suddenly.

Myers scrutinized each moment, movement and every object. He would draw diagrams, list material properties, note proximities and relationships to other objects forming a master taxonomy of the things that had occupied Dealey Plaza on November 22, 1963.

North Grassy Knoll:

- 3 x large traffic signposts
- 4 x sidewalk lamp posts
- John Neely Bryan north pergola concrete structure including 2 enclosed shelters
- Tool shed
- 1 x 3.3 foot (1 m) high concrete wall connected to each of the pergola shelters
- 10 x tall, wide, low-hanging live oak trees
- 5 foot (1.5 m) tall, wooden, cornered, stockade fenceline approx. 169 feet (53.6 m) long
- 6 street curb sewers openings, sewer manholes + interconnecting large pipes
- Various 2 to 6 foot (0.6 to 1.8 m) tall bushes, trees, and hedges.

Myers digital simulation of the Plaza grew. To assist, he built physical models which he could begin to inhabit. A 1:20 version of the grassy knoll, a 1:1 section of the Book Depository. Masking tape mapped out Elm Street over the studio floor. A desk stood in for the Presidential limousine. Myers walked around. He stood in Zapruders position. He stepped back and right as though he were standing behind the stockade fence. He crouched, occupying the space where Kennedy's head took the first impact of the bullet.

The physical and digital models grew in complexity, grew in their refinement as Myers fed more information into them. As he modeled, it expanded. The Triple Underpass was marked out into the parking lot. Slowly, Myers felt like a truth was emerging from his simulated landscapes, that the spatial mapping of the mass of accruing data was congealing into something solid.

In 2003, ABC News approached Myers to provide his Dealey Plaza recreation for its documentary special honoring the fortieth anniversary of President Kennedy's assassination. Myers was delighted. It would allow his project to become professional, not just a part-time hobby.

ABC provided him with production crew and a budget. Together, they worked through more and more information, increasing the resolution of the models.

They employed a team of researchers who sent bundles of fresh information daily. Sheathes of documents – detailing increasingly specific and isolated information: the make up of the roads tarmac, the humidity at the moment the shots were fired, autopsy reports, seasonal estimates of foliage density. These were distributed to the model making team. Key points were reconstructed in three dimensions for clarity, the results fed back into the digital model whose level of detail was becoming increasingly resolved.

Myers commissioned sculptor Mark Stuckey to create life-size clay busts of President Kennedy and Governor Connally so he could pay particular attention to their relative seating positions. Then, he covered the surface contours of each man's casting with a grid in order to import three-dimensional data points using a digital probe. With LightWave, he connected these data points and made accurate virtual models of both men's heads, and then connected them to generic models of human bodies that he had rigged for animation. The line between physical and virtual became blurred. Sections of rapidly prototyped models were outputted from the digital version, adjusted, rescanned.

Just at the point where Myers ambition seemed to be reaching a peak, he began to feel something strange. As the model became more accurate something seemed to be slipping away. The ABC crew continued to work, recreating the internal layouts of the Book Depository on blueprints provided by Burson, Hendricks & Walls for the Dallas County Depository restoration project in 1978. They crafted replicas of the presidential limousine, a 1961 Lincoln convertible, after the original body draft from The Hess & Eisenhardt Company.

Each time Myers looked, he seemed to see something slightly different. Each day, the models seemed to have changed. Slight alterations of angle, miniscule alterations of scale, almost imperceptible changes to the physics of the world he had created seemed to be happening. He couldn't be sure it wasn't simply his imagination. Real or not, his belief in his models as hard fact began to wane. Somehow they seemed to be drifting into their own fiction. Landscapes whose sole purpose it was to represent truth began to look grotesquely inaccurate. Perhaps they were being adjusted by somebody or something. Myers became increasingly suspicious that the ABC crew was not there to help him but to subvert his search for the truth.

Myers devised a plan to keep a check on this sensation. Back at home, he began to make a reference project – a model of his models. These would allow him to preserve key points of data, to double check the degree of subversion or distortions his imagination was exerting on his perception.

Increasingly, Myers retreated from the busy studio. He would leave earlier each day. Once home, he began work on a series of other models. These models were different. They explored the assassination outwards from the Plaza. They addressed the catalogues of material dealing with the wider context of the assassination. First, he made a miniature recreation of the Bay of Pigs. Up in the attic he worked on a series of reconstructions detailing the cabals of international bankers, the CIA, the Mafia. He made replicas of his reference material. A miniaturized version of the Warren Commission report, a scaled replica of the Zapruder film.

In these secret models, information overlaid information. Facts became complicated by other facts. Truths overtook other truths. Myers worked in increasing frenzy. Connections flashed like misfiring synapses over his models. He began to rework and rework, each model multiplying into others.

More and more information mapped itself over his house, increasingly complex narratives. Fragments of other narratives began to appear. As he read more, other patterns began to form in the miniature world around him:

Another key Brotherhood symbol is the pyramid or the pyramid with the capstone missing. The street plan of Dealey Plaza where Kennedy was killed is shaped like a pyramid with the capstone missing and Dealey actually means 'Goddess Line' as in Dea (goddess) and ley (ley line).

Everything he looked at suggested a collapse of history and geography. Suddenly, he would find himself driven by tangential narratives, nocturnally modeling from fragments of information. Plasticine landscapes spiraled in complex choreographies from one location to another. He mapped the Orion Constellation onto the Plaza, noting the coincidence of the red giant Sirius with the Dallas City Police parking lot. He modeled Oliver Stone in the Plaza shooting JFK, he tracked the relationship between Stone and the actor Woody Harrelson whose father was the first of the tramps arrested in one of the three railroad cars on the overpass.

It was impossible to model anything singularly. Everything depended upon everything else. Narratives overlaid one another. He built a 1:500 partial replica of Area 51 based upon a collection of speculative maps, long range photography and satellite imagery. And inside a hangar, he modeled a model of the Moons surface, and on this surface figurines of Stanley Kubrick and his younger brother Raul. He dug through his basement into his house's foundations to map a model of the Pont de l'Alma tunnel and a neo-forensic replica of Princess Diana's crashed Mercedes-Benz S280 W140.

One night, Myers improvised the Millennium Dome, Canary Wharf, Big Ben and Cleopatra's Needle in an effort to uncover an occult meaning of domes and obelisks. Comparing balsa wood models of Washington DC, the Pyramids and a plasticine model of Martian geography Myers examined similarities, looking for resonances extending across time and space. Reconstruction – the freezing of data, of scenarios into physical form – was a way of constructing pauses in his torrents of doubt. It seemed from these fragments that some kind of totalility might re-emerge, as though immersion in doubt, suspicion and paranoia was the only way to escape those same sensations of doubt, suspicion and paranoia.

Myers' replicas gave him brief respite from the manias that drove him, moments of solid certainty in a deluge of paranoia, before they sunk back into hazy phantom-ness.

Still, his suspicions of the ABC crew working on the Dealy model grew. Their work had slowed as the source information became more complex. It took them a month to work through changes in response to a second version of the Zapruder footage that had come to light. They had been comparing the various versions of the Zapruder films to examine claims that the footage itself was not a window into a moment, but another layer of conspiracy. Later, after a three-dimensional scan of the window in the Book Depository that Oswald supposedly fired from became problematic as another window with the same claim appeared on eBay. Certain features, such as a glob of paint on the glass, didn't match photos of the window taken moments after the assassination. Legal proceedings prevented the team from examining the second.

Myers paranoid double-model became equally problematic. He began to mistrust his secret models, as though the same malaise that had affected the studio model had spread. In response, he modeled his own house, his neighbors, and his street. He modeled his own interiors and within these, he made replicas of his own models to examine who might be observing him or what might be causing this drift away from fact. His models became absorbed into each other. And Myers too became a character in these simulations. His own movements, his own routine mapped in miniature.

His modeling became increasingly abstract. If others could understand the narratives of the replicas, it left him vulnerable to their manipulations. To prevent this, he began to replace literal models with other objects, enco-ding his landscapes of global conspiracy into everyday domesticity. In his bathroom, the position of soaps, of toothpaste, of marks traced into the condensation of the mirror marked out scenarios of extreme paranoia. The meanings of objects flowed into one another, both at the same time. And then something else.

Soon, the significance of domesticity had become entirely transformed. Myers reworked the stitching in a patchwork to mark relationships between international finance and the Bilderberg Group. Scratches in the surface of a coffee table indicated a potential description of the assassination of Yitzhak Rabin. Myers worked though his garden, replanting and resculpting to indicate relationships between the Owl of Wisdom, the Illuminati, the Bohemian Club, Schlaraffia and James Gordon Bennett Jr.

Soon, it became impossible for Myers to see his own house as a house. Its entire fabric and everything inside it betrayed a culture of total and complete crisis. It's every feature coded into a network of connections.

His suspicions continued to increase. Before long, he believed that even this cryptology was compromised. That any action, any object that he might move would reveal his intentions, that his whole edifice would unravel into the hands of his enemies.

While Myers' wild-eyed invisible imaginings unfolded, ABC began to wrap up their project. He had become increasing disengaged, unable to focus, unable to communicate with what seemed to be double agents encamped in his studio. As the final frames of their project rendered, Myers eyes flitted around nervously, as if the very walls would begin to speak the deepest and darkest secrets in plain voice.

As the crew left, Myers determined to dispose of his models as fast as possible. He could only see their explicitness as a kind of betrayal. That their clarity of narrative only served to disguise their falseness. That their representation of truth – whatever truth it might have once suggested: lone gunman, multiple shooters...he couldn't quite recall, and it seemed to no longer matter – was a clarity that only served to confuse. That any fact simply hid another. As he crushed the Herz sign, plucked the Umbrella man, crumpled the Stockade Fence, flattened the Grassy Knoll their destruction seemed to release more than their intricate constructions could have ever revealed. The miniature ruin of the Plaza, flattened by a monstrous sized Myers was now a potential fiction conjoined with the other multiple narratives. And all of them existed at the same time. His giant hand reaching down from the sky, Oswald's bullet impacting the Presidents skull, a bead of his sweat falling on the Triple Bypass at exactly the same moment that gunshots were fired.

Myers worked all night, dismantling everything. Landscapes piled up on each other. Fragments of one crushed themselves into another. Scaled models of the Vatican broke into pieces over a cast of the Ark of the Covenant. A detailed model of Marilyn Monroe receiving a rectally administered barbiturate enema shattered into pieces.

By morning, Myers stood in what seemed to be an ordinary home. Everything his paranoid manias had driven him to physically form was gone. Instead, a clock ticked, sunlight fell through the window reflecting in the gloss of mahogany. But in this silence, objects seemed to be in crisis, their meanings fluctuating, flickering, disappearing, merging with others in a contagious chain at hysterical speed.

Next morning, as Myers drove into the studio, every movement of his car seemed to be re-enacting movements that came from somewhere else. As he took a corner, he felt as if moments of history were being replayed through him. The highway itself seemed held some kind of coded meaning, and he and all the other drivers were acting out hidden significances, blips in a geographically scaled occult diagram. Through the windscreen, the landscape as far as the horizon performed as a cypherous model.

Everything seemed to be endlessly on the verge of resolution, while simultaneously on the verge of total collapse. All of history converged in every object in a concentration of complete apocalypse. Everything is implicated, and nothing is innocent. ∎

AN URBANISM

OF

INTERIORS

JEANNETTE
RODRÍGUEZ'S
PARLIAMENT

by Andrés Jaque

In the rhetoric of everyday life the living room is the centre of the home, the depoliticised den, the 'independent republic of your house'. A capsule of intimacy that is characterised by leaving what is held in common and its frictions outside. The intimate excludes the commonly held. The living room is that comfortable wing chair, the place where we find our slightly out-of-date slippers, and that record with a song that's on the odd side, but which we really like. At a time of generic airports and repetitive outskirts, the living room is specific and particular, and is mildly free of those polemical processes in which the collective fights among itself. In the rhetoric of everyday life the living room confirms us as individuals disconnected from what is shared, in an interior protected from that predictable climatology we tend to call the public domain.

But what remains to the rest of us in this zoning of the political?

The material agoras of the commonly held seem to be on hand and to be forever neutral, like white canvases, inorder to be occupied by different manifestos, changing activities and irritating conflicts. Public space, and to a great extent contemporary architecture, does not dirty its hands with what occurs in it; it simply serves as a support without adding anything, without facing up to things. Political action seems to be posterior to the street; it begins when everything is built. Unlike the living room, the architecture of the spaces in which the collective is instituted, in much of the prevailing rhetoric, acts as the elegant background to a daily round of the uncertain and the conflictive, like the mirror that forms automatic images of the uneven textures we call societies. But something has occurred this afternoon in this house that leads me to think that everything's a bit different, in fact.

LA DAMA DE ROSE. JOSÉ IGNACIO CABRUJAS & LUIS MANZO. CARACAS 1986 – 87.

This living room is on the far-flung outskirts of Madrid, and it has a TV. It also has a sofa, covered in flowery chintz.

The TV is on and reproduces the moving image of a sofa, also covered in flowers. On it Jeannette Rodriguez listens to a fellow cast member with a black moustache, who says to her, "But if the two of you love each other, and you love him more than anyone else in the world, then love each other!"

It's La dama de rosa – The Lady in Pink – a Venezuelan TV series from 1986. Gabriela (Jeannette Rodriguez), in love with and made pregnant by the wealthy Tito Clemente, was accused of a crime she never committed. After seven years in prison, she's returned with her skin darkened and her hair dyed and under the false identity of Emperatriz Ferrer, in order, by seducing Clemente once again, to revenge herself for how, when the going got tough, he turned his back on her.

In the scene, her friend David, who knows her as Emperatriz, encourages her to give in to love, without realising that in so doing he is pushing her to wreak her revenge. The music gets louder. The two embrace. Close up of Jeannette: "Yes, it's true, David. I love him." The camera draws closer to the main protagonist's face. She smiles the way someone who has found true love might, but the smile immediately changes into a look of concern. Her involvement is nothing but the point of no return of the attack on the man she loves and at the same time hates. Jeannette closes her eyes and purses her lips, while she is held in a curious embrace, half paternalist, half lascivious, by the young David.

Brusquely the scene changes. Jeannette is standing in the same living room. David is no longer with her, however. Instead, there's Dalila Colombo, who plays Leyla, Clemente's official girlfriend, who sorrowfully announces to her that she's decided to leave him. Close up of Leyla: "I'm referring to the fact that I'm stepping out of Tito's life."

Close up of Emperatriz and an intense, shrill sound, like the Casiotone home synthesiser: "That I'm not going to marry him", says Leyla.

And here comes the key moment.

Very big close up of Jeannette, who looks at Leyla while the shrill sound becomes moderately unbearable. She looks at Leyla, but not entirely. She looks through Leyla, at somewhere close to the infinite. A look like a soldier in formation who knows that his commanding officer is not the one who gives the orders, but an entire country, which he serves with his actions.

This is the typical look which, along with the shrill tone of the Casiotone, is used to conclude many of the scenes in Venezuelan TV series. Which is the look that constructs the grammar of the TV series that get on the nerves of film critics, who don't understand that it isn't Leyla that Jeannette is seeking beyond the camera.

On the other sofa, the one in the living room in the outskirts of Madrid, the tone puts us all, or at least my mother, my sister and me, who're following the series, on the spot.

To love in order to take revenge? Or will there be room in that same love, which began as revenge, for forgiveness? Social justice, in a promotional marriage? Or access to the family that strengthens the perpetrator of the affront, in order, thereby, to undermine the institution that furthers the injustice? Aren't these issues the ones that have given rise to a major part of the public disputes of the last two centuries?

My sister on the sofa, arguing with my mother and me, emerges as a citizen with an opinion: "Let her marry the pig and two-time him with all his friends." Me: "Won't that be insufficient punishment?" My mother: "Is it worth living just to take your revenge?"

ANDRÉS Mr. Morley, why didn't the thinkers of the early Frankfurt School liketelevision? Why did they see in it a system of alienation and an elimination of social complexity?

DAVID MORLEY Let's say that their vision was socially naive. They only paid attention to the contents of television, as if from the TV to the sofa there weren't ways of questioning this, as if they weren't social constructs.
The contents are spaces of discussion, in some cases spaces of provocation, even.

ANDRÉS But why is the music so bad?

DAVID MORLEY It's certainly crude, but it manages to create a break in which your mother, your sister and you install yourselves in Emperatriz's diatribe, and also in the choices David and Leyla defend.

ANDRÉS But the arguing is endless. It's never resolved.

DAVID MORLEY That is in fact what annoys many moderns: peace never arrives. Our public space is not neutral and the material it is built of is dispute.
There are no happy endings, because there are always contrasting interests and sensibilities.

ANDRÉS Mr. Morley, I suspect that architecture is the constructing of a living room. A living room with a TV that encourages us to emerge as citizens embracing a position. Architecture is the constructing of a speechifying in which there will never be agreement, but in which we will be able to carry on together. It isn't science that resolves the problems, but political construction that makes the coexistence of the controversial possible.

Our house is number 3C in a block of flats with a garden. In the block next door, there's a chemist's and a small supermarket. A kilometre away is the school my sister and I went to, the same one we vote in now.

Are we to believe that the space between the supermarket and the school, that succession of flowerbeds, is the place we turned into citizens in? Is this our space of socialisation?

I believe urbanism has fled from these places and is constructed wherever it gives rise to difference. The city is the space that remains between the chintz sofa on which my mother, my sister and I spend the afternoon, and the image created by electric devices of a sofa with a similar chintz on which Emperatriz does something like spending the afternoon with David and Leyla. An in-between two spheres that mutually imitate and question one another, to which we connect ourselves as citizens who choose to participate in the dispute of shared fictions, in experiments that contain all that falls to our lot as a collective.

This is not a canvas in white, it's a space constructed with dangerous choices and the need to take sides when faced with them.

The house is the place in which our everyday life connects up with what we desire as members of a collective. The place in which in arguing and saying if we separate out the rubbish or not we turn into citizens who share an ideal image of themselves within a society.

ANDRÉS Mr. Wallace, is the space between the sofa and the electronic image of a sofa a mirror?

DAVID FOSTER WALLACE If it were, it wouldn't be the mirror that automatically creates our images as members of a collective, I reckon it would seem more like the mirror in which adolescent boys, after doing weights in their bedroom, verify how their body begins to look like the image of their own body they yearn after and which makes them form part of the group of those who yearn after a muscular body.

My sister, my mother and I live in an in-between.

In between those fictions that we take heed of, hate, analyse and pass judgement on, and a sofa in number 3C of a block of flats with a chemist's on the corner.

Experiencing how our life comes close to or moves away from these fictions is what we do. It's what my sister does when arguing in sustainability blogs about what's the best way of separating out the rubbish or the most efficient way of stacking the dishwasher. It's what we do when we compare our birthday with Queen Fabiola's, as photographed in Hola magazine. It's what we do when we 'laboratorise' the house with the women neighbours so that my Aunt Margarita demonstrates live to them the advantages of the Tupperware digital seal.

To belong to the architects' collage, to the tennis club, to the group of housewives on the housing estate or to the informal network of those who consider themselves to be eco-sensitive, it's necessary to live in an in-between in which one experiments by exploring the distance between what is and what might be.

This, in part, is what being a citizen in my barrio is, and wherever this occurs is where the city appears. The group therapies, the newspaper stands, the betting shops, the discothèques, the hairdressing parlours, the neighbourhood sports centre, the gym and its mirrors, the supermarket, the direct method Berlitz class, the Internet forums, match.com, the dark rooms, the psychoanalyst's consulting room, the mail order catalogues, the UV cabins and the Tupperware gatherings are the Central Park it has fallen to our lot to experience. A city of interiors, in which we turn into citizens by reacting to committed discourses. By measuring and inscribing publicly and experimentally our distance from the fictions that decorate the spaces we share in the distance.

JEANNETTE Darling, what is it that keeps on changing us? What is the motor of the city? Why so much speechifying?

ANDRÉS it isn't progress. It isn't justice. I believe it's simply desire, as in any ecosystem. The city is the space of the erotic. We desire, and by desiring we join forces and create disputes in collective experiments. I think this is what we've been calling politics, and that's the material one urbanises with.

POLTERGEIST. TOBE HOOPER. LOS ANGELES 1982.

If someone were to ask me for a photo of our city of interiors, I'd know exactly what to give them.

I'd send them the poster of Poltergeist.

It's a portrait format poster. At the bottom there's a photo of the California suburb where the Freelings lived, with its ridge roofs, its garages, its front lawns and its winding streets. Given the gradation of the sky from red to yellow, the suburb seems to be right in the middle of sunset, in a kind of golden moment.

And at the top there's the main character, Carol Anne, seen from inside the TV set.

It might have been a cellphone connected to an Internet forum, it might have been a song by the Velvet Underground or some platinum-blonde locks of hair, but without these little devices for politically urbanising in the distance, the Freelings' interiors would have been no more than just that: interiors. ■

SCENES FROM A CITY

by Triin Ojari

CITY-THEMING

I t was the first deliberate city-theming to take place in Tallinn.

All was in place in the old industrial quarter, where rich clients attracted by promises of everything 'cool' were to be accommodated in alluring lofts and studios, with every imaginable facility at close hand: cinemas, cafes, art galleries, trendy shops and expensive bars; the 15-minute walk to the shopping centers in the heart of town; the magical charm of the old town; the city's passenger harbor and the smell of the sea air within reach.

This type of potential-packed empty space was common to many post-Soviet city centers, but in Tallinn the area between the city centre and the sea had remained unused for a long time. During the initial moments in the rampant neoliberalist performance, the first capitalist cowboys did not manage to devour it and transform it into a plastic shopping center. This came only in the second moment, fueled by the idea "lets do business, but differently" – that is, more expensively.

Already decades ago culture had been on sale in Soho, and now it was time for Estonian yuppies to sell their four-wheel drives and move from the suburbs back to the city.

The Young Architect liked the sea breeze blowing between the buildings. This new-old quarter right in the heart of the city was his first big break. Well, actually not the first, because like many of his generation, who had graduated not too long ago, he too had many private houses to his name, some in pine forests, others among firs, in the middle of sand dunes and some in open fields.

There was plenty of space in Estonia.Even close to the capital a plot measuring a few 1000 square meters was considered normal and no one shied away from eye-catching, unique houses.

And of course there were competitions – during the last decade the winners of public architecture competitions were rarely over the age of 35. Why do we need Europan?

The Young Architect was the child of the new Photoshop generation and knew which buttons to press. With each competition design he was able to create a convincing impression and in every race he gained a place on the pedestal.

This was before the building boom, and imagery meant everything. Virtual images of potential worlds, cities and buildings convinced the client, and the architect too, that everything would be beautiful.

At that time no one was actually building anything. But now everyone was, and the boom had devoured even the last of the naïve.

The Young Architect traveled a lot and liked European cities, with all their trimmings – the cafes, the street paving, the markets, the small scale and the close-knit communities. Tallinn had the Hanseatic old town, but everything beyond the medieval walls was an eternal fringe – too poor to be dense and unified. And everyone was in too much of a hurry to finish anything properly anyway.

Tallinn was made available for the self-made man. The city had become a stormy current with various bits floating around like islands, each moving in a different direction.

The Young Architect too, was able to create his own city within this current, to create something completely new, a collage of his travels, his urban passions, and experiments built in the pine forests.

His clients understood that the age of gluing new façades onto old buildings had passed and the city had to be built differently – by faking it, if necessary. Let the Architect have fun, let him import super-small paving stones from Portugal, let him bend strange patterns from metal pipes and model buildings using handmade bricks so that each building has a unique pattern! (The moulds for the bricks were later destroyed – just to make sure.) And so the Young Architect created a square, the most important and most clichéd element at the heart of a European city, around which life is centered.

The lower floors are zoned for business and there are apartments above. He envisages only small shops and corner bars that serve fresh pastries to the locals in the mornings.

Over the last ten years Tallinn had become a city for tourists, speeding cars and spreading mega-supermarkets in ever increasingly peripheral areas.

The Young Architect's quarter was to be a rebirth of the city.

True, he didn't have enough time or power to allow for the processes to take place naturally, to allow the people and the buildings to find their own place, as in a real city, or to be surprised by the hybrid city functions that occurred by themselves.

Everything had to be done immediately, and at the very least they could strive to achieve diversity and a sense of the back-alley, so that there would at least be this feeling left.

Furthermore, every square meter was accounted for, and it was expensive. Long ago, the city had sold the land along with the factory buildings and it was no longer 'our' space, but 'their' space. And 'they', together with the persuasive Young Architect, were able to make it their own city. They masked their business plans with cultural festivals, photography exhibitions, fashion shows, cutting edge-designed street furniture and a summer farmer's market with specially designed barrows.

Instead of one Young Architect there were already many of them working in the quarter. For those who know how to make new architecture fit in with the old by using rust-colored façades, and for those whose specialty it is to make an unexpected extension to an old roof.

Come on! We're in an old factory! Everyday-rules of normality and beauty don't exist.

If necessary, we'll make a glass and metal tower for the roof.

We'll make three if you like.

The architects have convinced the client and the city is now full of the unexpected.

Now, we just have to come up with the surprises.

FENG SHUI

The Client is in a bad mood.

He has done everything by the book. His quarter should be a local success story of urban improvement.

He has put too much money into this – especially for a local property developer who usually gets by as cheaply as possible, it was an unheard-of sum of money.

But the boom came to an end too soon, and completed residential and business premises turned from speculative gold into non-winning lottery tickets.

The Client knew commercial success depended on directing the traffic of people and ensnaring the potential consumer.

Tallinn had never been a consistently planned city. Thus it is suddenly made clear that a lump of a building built some ten years ago stands between the client's recently completed magical land and the throbbing city centre.

This building has no windows because it houses a cinema. And it lacks thoroughfares and an active ground floor because all the entertainment takes place inside darkened rooms on glowing screens.

This building could be anywhere, but unfortunately for our client it stands right in his way and is indifferent to its surroundings.

But maybe things are not so simple and the city's energy is an unseen world which requires a greater power to capture it? Maybe the visible physical space manages to generate unseen energy, to direct the flow of people and create atmosphere.

But what may determine these forces?

The Client is familiar with the oriental martial arts and believes in unseen forces.

He engages a Feng Shui Master to analyze his city.

Something under ground or between the buildings must be wrong, because the square is pretty and the aprons worn by the market sellers are clean, and the rusty façade has a feeling of history, and the program of events made to attract the city folks has been prepared a year in advance…

The Master paints a picture of underground rivers and negative energy fields that the naked eye cannot see, but which float above the new city.

On the surface everything is in place – this is still the old industrial quarter, where rich clients attracted by promises of everything 'cool' were to be accommodated in alluring lofts and studios, with every imaginable facility at close hand: cinemas, cafes, art galleries, trendy shops and expensive bars...

Some things are just simply beyond our power.

SUBURBIA, WINTER 2020

J had driven this road to work every morning for ten years now.

The changing views beyond the windscreen provided a fairly good picture of the ebb and flow of Estonia's economic successes.

As in the sea, some places had suddenly become exposed like reefs, some had become completely barren and people had fled leaving the shipwreck behind to withstand its fate.

J's car was not the newest model, but it was a four-wheel drive and it had been useful to face the condition of the roads in his home suburb during the winter months.

J had been a middle manager in a large Swedish owned bank for many years.

The severe economic decline during the previous five years robbed him of his bonuses and travel incentives, but nothing more.

J was musing that it had been good that they had sold all their large companies to the Scandinavians, as the newspapers heralded at the time. "They won't leave us high and dry", he thought.

Unfortunately, many of J's neighbors and the thousands who bought homes in the suburbs during the boom did not fare so well.

There was a time when it was easy to get a bank loan. The banks were handing them out left, right and centre because these same banks were just as happy to lend to developers to buy land and build houses. They were interested in clients on all fronts.

Everything went on sale because money was cheap and the Prime Minister promised that within 15 years Estonia would be among the five richest countries in Europe!

That time had now arrived but there were no riches to be seen anywhere.

Driving past the open fields, J saw half-finished and empty houses and apartment blocks. Some were now inhabited by dubious characters that had moved in of their own volition. Some of the larger ones had become community or cultural centers. Some were advertised as prizes in lotteries. Others were just left to rot.

Break there. Stop!

Although when the economic decline was at its toughest the massive peak-hour traffic jams on the main roads leading into the city virtually disappeared because of the high oil prices, Now the traffic jams seem to be back. Nothing has changed...

During the Soviet period there were few single-family houses and these could be built only according to strict plans and could not be more than 60 square meters. It was no surprise that with re-independence houses swelled into palaces like birthday cakes, and the city began to spread onto the surrounding fields.

The custom of hiring an architect remained. Land was cheap and the need for an architect was still etched in people's memories from the long distant Soviet era, as a reminiscence of the need to differentiate oneself from the surrounding standardised environment. One wanted to be the landlord in one's own tiny world.

And playing in a small way at being Western was also very strong. To get a plot of land was paramount. What the house looked like or how it was built was not important, and as a rule neither the developer nor the local government cared either. Often no one cared about the infrastructure either. That's why the roads in the new residential areas remained unsealed and in spring the melting snow transformed the roads into inaccessible mud rivers.

"Gosh, today the line of cars seems to be endless!" J exclaimed.

"Why do people move to the outskirts?"

Out of boredom, he started to play with the possibilities.

"Because they grew up in a single-family house and they had a happy childhood. Because they grew up in an ugly dormitory suburb of prefabricated apartment blocks. Because the sandpits were communal and it wasn't safe to go out at night. Because every magazine and television program promoted the idea of your own house..."

For the successful family, moving out of the city was the promise of happiness – an address they could be proud of.

Actually, the suburb where J lived was different.

It wasn't a mishmash of different styles.

The houses had all been designed by one architect. It was a well-planned area with economical houses. It was the first such suburb in Tallinn where the public sector, in this case the city, rented the land to the developer and commissioned proper architecture for the area.

Initially, the area was unkindly nicknamed 'concentration camp' because of the blocky shape of the houses, but that kind of minimalism was actually fashionable at the time.

Modernism was not as fashionable in Estonia as it was in Finland or Holland, but J's house was designed by one of Estonia's more prominent architects, one who had become known for designing luxury white villas for the local elite.

Now all of the 200 homeowners in J's suburb could have a taste of being the elite: windows to the floor, straight walls, flat roofs and high ceilings in the living room.

J had seen that Scandinavia and Western Europe were full of such uniform residential areas, but there weren't so many in Estonia.

J was proud of the ideal of equality in his home suburb – the sameness of the houses wore the image of the Western social democracy that had never managed to take root in Estonia. The Soviet collective society was too fresh a memory.

The sameness somehow echoed that everyone believed overwhelmingly that hard work would bring freedom, even though this actually meant buying one's freedom bit-by-bit from the bank.

Break again!

Turning into the car park, J yawned.

He had left home an hour ago – the morning rush hour was no joke.

But over the years he had learned how to steer, eat breakfast and shave all at the same time. Everyone did this.

CITY AND FREEDOM

Roland had worked in the city planning office for years and was responsible for the architectural appearance of the city.

In name he was the boss, but Roland didn't really have any power.

He wasn't a politician and unfortunately city affairs were determined by the interests of the party, the wishes of sponsors, beneficial contracts, elections etc.

These shenanigans prevented long term urban planning strategies and discussions about the suitability of one design or another. Roland had thick skin; otherwise he would not have lasted in the job so long.

His department was ten times smaller than that of the Finns, their neighbors across the gulf. What level of thoroughness and forward planning must prevail in town planning there!

It was no wonder that in Tallinn, where all the land had been sold to private owners long ago, planning was also done by the private sector – you can't do it all yourself! Let the owners divide and design.

In the eyes of rampant liberalist economic policy any kind of interference by the public sector would have spelled death to the freedom of business interests.

Roland could not deny that there was a lot in Tallinn, and in Estonia for that matter, that was architecturally very interesting. The fast pace had left 'air holes', in which original solutions can flourish without great difficulty.

Only recently in the newspaper a young architect from Western Europe admiringly called Tallinn a 'laboratory' and said that the city was large enough to try out all kinds of ideas. Even bad ideas – Roland knew this all too well.

All those respectable Scandinavian businessmen filling this Eldorado with all kinds of squares and parks, introducing the local consumer to new shopping centers full of well-calculated traps and dead ends.

Roland had seen from his office window how a few dozen local activists with Estonian flags had been protecting a limestone and marble communist party conference centre built a couple of decades ago during the dying days of the Soviet Union – what an ideological melodrama! In the corridors, the party condoned the new owner's plan to demolish this 'lump of ice' in the centre of town and build a post-ideological mega-super-hyper centre with cinemas and shops all mixed up together, in the manner of British 'anything goes'-architecture.

The people with the flags had protected the building, as one of the last remaining large-scale buildings from that period.

Suddenly the diversity of the urban space in Eldorado had become important … until the excavator arrived the next morning.

Is it possible to symbolize freedom?

During the time that Roland had been in his job, skyscrapers had grown up next to decaying wooden houses, and private capital, aware of its rights and freedoms, had grabbed a large chunk of the public space.

Roland was tolerant. He believed it wasn't important what the buildings looked like, but rather the message they spoke.

Tallinn's physical incompleteness and its cacophonic streetscape spoke of freedom.

But now, suddenly, the politicians had reached a consensus that Estonia's freedom should be embodied in a monument.

Roland always felt embarrassed when he passed the newly unveiled column of Liberty on the city's main square. For the first time the state powers had assumed the role of art censors and with carefully selected tools had delivered a sharp blow to the fresh ideas sprouting from the 'air holes'.

Enough of this modern pushing of boundaries and critical discourse, paradigmatic programs and modern fluff.

Estonian freedom was now symbolised by a 24-metre glass cross on the edge of the main square. It was a bulky anachronistic symbol, a powerful counter-attack by traditionalists. Enough of self-searching in dimly lit borderlands.

In the globalizing world, Estonia was now held on course by a monument that immortalized its historical struggle for freedom by undertaking a form reminiscent of a tombstone.

Roland's arms dropped to his side.

Powerless, he felt a choking sensation. ∎

All resemblance to real events or persons is entirely coincidental.

THE DARK SIDE OF THE MODERN

by Emiliano Gandolfi

can't say what makes me keep coming back to this place. I don't think it is the acrid smell of glue and excrement, and not even the joyful laughter and pranks of the children in the neighborhood.

Probably I'm attracted by something less palpable: I want to understand a widespread, yet neglected dynamic, to immerse myself in a fundamental dimension of the growth of our metropolises, in the dark side of the modern.

Raksha and Praku have lived here for two generations. They're among the six million citizens of Mumbai who live in homes they've built with their own hands. Over a million of them occupy the piece of land named Dharavi. Multitudes dwelling in a sensitive membrane which changes shape continuously: an immense expanse of corrugated iron, sheets of PVC, pillars made from scavenged materials, all gathered together to form a single continuous sheltering surface.

Viewed from above, the city is divided into two distinct masses. One consists of orderly buildings aligned in rigid street axes flanked by palm trees and ficus. The other is the district where Raksha and Praku live. It is a dense, fluid mass. Shapeless in its complexity, it spreads without a break.

The boundary between these two different worlds is always a zone of conflict, and is continually redefined.

Today Dharavi is creeping southward with the addition of twenty new families, refugees from the floods in Bengal. A little further north, it changes from cardboard to galvanized sheet metal filched by night from the construction site of the Bandra Kurla skyscraper, marooned by the financial meltdown.

Tomorrow, perhaps, will be the day of the police raid. It happens every month. Hundreds of shacks are demolished in the vain effort to expel hundreds of thousands of people from the soft underbelly of the city. The very city that first attracted them, helped them, gave them hope and at times expelled them to its margins, ruthlessly excludes them.

At sunset I always come and sit on these rocks, seeking momentary refuge from the fierce pulsing of the city. I gaze at the steady flow of pilgrims to the islet with the mausoleum of Haji Ali. Raksha and Praku often accompany me. We consider it our moment of meditation, an interval when the pressures of the city around us are suspended. Here we swap reflections on the day that has passed.

Squatting not far from us is Raksha. Over and over again he sings the same refrain from Jodhaa Akbar, the movie we saw the other night at the Eros cinema. Hrithik Roshan, one of the Bollywood stars most in vogue at the moment, played Akbar the Great. The most important of the Mughal emperors was famed not just for the unprecedented expansion of his empire and love of the arts, but also for his attempt to fuse the religions of the period into a single cult of universal brotherhood.

In 1992/93 Dharavi was the setting of violent attacks and reprisals between Muslims and Hindus. Here this message sounds like the distant echo of tensions cooling and being regularly rekindled through the centuries. Thanks to this film, Akbar the Great became a mythological figure among all the children. For weeks the whole district was pervaded by his message of brotherhood. But other, far from peaceful messages, like those of the Hindu nationalist party Shiv Sena, could just as well find an echo in the streets in the months ahead, awakening ancestral resentments.

Praku, Raksha's inseparable brother, sits insistently close to me, squeezing my arm, as is his way, to stress the climactic moments of his story. His eyes shine as they do whenever he talks about April 7, the now mythical day of the occupation of the railway tracks. His excitement is magnetic and the very quality that five years ago led me to contact the groups struggling for the rights of slum dwellers.

In telling his story Praku has his own special way of creating climaxes. He fires off short phrases uttered in rapid succession, rather like bursts of machine-gun fire, with short intervals when he seems to relax, pauses and looks up with a hopeful smile. The final effect is a fusion of opposites, reality and hope, fears and possibilities, in a rhythm that seems to reflect the contrasts of the world he lives in.

On April 7, Praku and a group of activists performed an act of opposition unprecedented in the history of the struggle for housing in Mumbai. Together they massed on the tracks of the urban railway. Exactly at the point where the northbound line, coming from Churchgate station and Victoria Terminus (now renamed Chatrapati Shivaji Terminus by Shiv Sena), forks off into the line that heads northeast and continues up along the coast. The most crucial junction in Mumbai, the fulcrum of the city, on the southern boundary of their quarter of Dharavi.

It took just a couple of hundred people to bring the whole city to its knees. That simple act left thousands trapped in the stuffy carriages of Indian Railways and Mumbai Suburban Railway. Trains packed with commuters who travel every day from the residential districts to the north to offices in the business heart of the city to the south.

The dull humming of the ventilators, the contact of skin on skin, the sweat of the rush hour mixed with agitation about the increasingly dramatic

delay. A struggle for survival in one of the world's biggest metropolises.
In those few hours on April 7, the balance of power was inverted.

The residents of Dharavi, those hundreds of thousands of outcasts,
had succeeded in blocking the city and stopping business, in an intermi-
nable suspended sigh. Mumbai was shaken by their protesting voices.
At that moment the chai wallahs (tea bearers), taxi drivers, bricklayers,
seamstresses, were no longer tiny cogs in the multibillion-dollar machine
of the city. Their act showed they were decisive, as they seized the power
previously denied them.

I wait for the right moment to make a confession to Praku. Just a few
hours ago I discovered what fate holds for them. There's a ruthless plan to
drive them down even lower in the city's heartless hierarchy. To destroy, in
just a few days, the years of laborious gains, of stands made, of social
relationships formed. And to dramatically dispel their economic networks,
built up laboriously over the years in the district.

Just a few hours ago I was sitting on the plush sofa of the cocktail
lounge of Taj Lands End Hotel. With me were Mukesh M., director of the
'Dharavi Redevelopment Project' project, and Gautam C., the city official
instructed to carry it out. On the pretext of an interview, I had sought a
meeting to try and learn something about the plans they were hatching.

With broad gestures, M. explained, without mincing his words, the
clean sweep he was going to make. But despite his practiced rhetoric and
point-by-point exposition, his words implied he was well aware of the
struggle he faced with the thousands of inhabitants of the district. April 7
had set a precedent and M. knew it.

He did not exclude the use of force, but he clearly preferred persuasion
and a stealthy, insinuating approach.

At times, fascinated by his manner and his skilful use of persuasive
phrases, I felt myself being led away by the breadth of his visionary three-
billion dollar plan: we have to go vertical, houses for all, give people the
opportunity to integrate with the mainstream, get rid of all the polluting
industries... Finally, in one last burst of eloquence, emphasized by a
carefully studied pause in which he opened his eyes wide and smiled
expansively, he ticked off a five-point strategy on his fingertips: HIKES –
Health, Income, Knowledge, Environment, Social.

Perhaps if I had not lived with the very people M. wanted "to integrate
into modernity" I would have believed him. All the same, it was still not clear
how they would get a million people to leave their homes and let the
bulldozers do their work.

M. took a deep breath and sat back on the sofa, giving me a soothing
smile. At that point C. began to list the organizational details: 236 hectares,
rehabilitate non-polluting industries, 57,000 rehab units, 42 amenities,
buildings that will become tourist attractions, sustainable development ...
His tone was more restrained, couched in wary and articulate bureaucratic

language. He seemed to be reciting an inevitable list of events learned by heart.

Finally he raised his eyes absently from that same point on the inlaid colonial table he had been gazing at all through his monologue. I took the opportunity to catch C. off guard and compelled him to answer a question.

At this M. became animated, shaking his hands in denial: no one would be forced to leave, clearly. They would redistribute apartments to the 57,000 families who owned their own home units and, he was careful to state with a magnanimous air, each old unit would be matched by 21 square meters in the new plan.

These figures were already familiar to me. I also knew from the activists of the National Slum Dwellers Federation (NSDF) that the total number of home units was actually 90,000. The census commissioned by the City Council had ignored all homes on the upper floors. Besides, this plan included only families resident before 2000 and it ignored the many informal businesses active in the district.

At that point M. turned to C. and spoke to him peremptorily in Hindi. Unsmiling, but with an air of obvious satisfaction, C. handed me a large volume with plastic spiral binding. He responded enthusiastically to my questioning look, emphasizing his words and nodding his head: "Here are the first 12,000 signatures by residents of Dharavi authorizing us to proceed."

A shudder ran down my back, ice-cold from the relentless air conditioning, which for the last hour had forced me to cover my belly with my arms. After many evenings spent discussing tactics of resistance to eviction, I now saw clearly what the strategy would be to induce the residents of Dharavi to leave. It was to buy their consent by bribing them with the hope of becoming an integral part of the system.

Simple. Lured by the promise of a lump sum and a micro-apartment of their own, thousands of residents had eagerly accepted the offer. They were unaware that once they left their homes they would never be allowed to return. And even in the best of all possible worlds, and in the unlikely event they really were given an apartment of their own in the new skyscraper district, they could never afford the management costs for such a property. They would end up being evicted into some other city slum. The whole history of the right to the city and its denial was starting all over again, an apparently endless cycle.

Raksha finally comes over to us with a cheery air. He is no longer singing, but from his swaying movements he still seems to be dancing soundlessly to a Bollywood tune. I take advantage of the brief interval to tell of my meeting that afternoon and to express my desolation.

Praku immediately grows serious. He stares fixedly at the sea, in the darkness of the night that now has fallen. His eyes narrow and his natural crouching position becomes rigid, as if he is drawing himself together, making himself smaller. Then with his cadenced accent and a hiss in his voice he whispers his dismay.

A city of 14 million people cannot keep going without hundreds of thousands of builders' laborers, dishwashers, secretaries, drivers, servants. The very skyscrapers that are the symbol of India's rebirth were the reason for the occupation of many of these informal districts scattered about the city. The workers on the construction sites had to live somewhere, so they built temporary homes right next to where they worked. At first the authorities allowed them to squat on the land. They thought they could raze the shacks when the skyscrapers were completed. But demographic pressures made these districts so dense and highly structured they became impregnable.

Modernity cannot live without someone to build it, but Mumbai seems to deny a refuge to its own lymph, these six million slum dwellers. They are the people who make the city function, but are asked to remain invisible, to live elsewhere and respect the ruthless laws of the market, that very market from which they are excluded.

At Dharavi I had got to know a number of families. Some had moved to the dormitory suburbs north of the city, some to Navi Mumbai, on the far side of the bay. They were usually the better-off families, with children who had studied and become professionals or gained a post in some IT business.

You often encountered difficulties if you said you lived in a 'village', the term commonly used in Mumbai for the various squatter islands within the city.

Most of the middle classes never set foot in one. They carefully avoided any reference to this ambivalent dimension of the city.

When families move out they finally attain a new standard of living. They have two rooms instead of one, a private bathroom instead of latrines used by 700 people daily. They have a kitchen, but above all they have a front door, an impassable threshold of privacy, non-existent in the districts of 'informal housing'. That door represents modern living, in contrast with the countryside or the slums, where life is collective: people eat together, sleep together, defecate together, wash together, and learn from one another.

When the mothers of the families tell their stories, it is wonderful to see joy light up their eyes as they describe the details of that precious home attained after generations of sacrifices, of badly paid toil and caste discrimination. But at some point in the story, their tone inevitably changes.

Mumbai is the world's most densely populated city, so it is also extremely expensive. The only affordable districts for the lower-middle class are far from the city's nerve centers or any place where they can earn a living. The expanses of residential skyscrapers are segregated from the city and lack all facilities. On the outside the buildings look finished, but often the technical plant has never been installed, the elevators are always out of order and public transport is a grueling ordeal.

Even the front door, the symbol of affluence, becomes a barrier in the imagination of the new residents. It's an obstacle to the kind of neighborly life they left behind, with helpful neighbors, a dense network of services and a sense of community, all of which are crucial when people have nothing else they can count on.

The Mumbai 'villages' essentially form islands existing in a paradoxical time mode. They are both archaic and extremely modern. Places where thousands of interwoven parallel economies plug the gaps in the surrounding system, but where social relationships are much the same as those in the countryside, with close-knit, supportive communities.

After attaining the goal of affluence, after buying an apartment and no longer having to lie about their origins, many families decide to return to the 'villages'. At first they may have difficulty readapting to the oppressive overcrowding, but gradually and with a little investment they do up their shack, build masonry walls and add two upper floors. Sometimes they even plant shrubs in the tiny space in front, jealously protected from the ravenous goats that wander loose in the streets.

Raksha and Praku come from one such family. Their eldest brother graduated in electronic engineering. He became service head of an English call centre based in Gamdevi, just off Chowpatty Beach, the city's most popular beach and the best place to eat Bhelpuri.

After spending two years on the twenty-fifth floor of a skyscraper in the Thane district, some thirty kilometers north of the centre, they decided to return to Dharavi. Their family was welcomed back joyfully by Social Nagar, the neighborhood where they lived before moving out. At first they shared a room, but now they finally have a place of their own.

After returning Praku became an NSDF activist. A month ago Raksha got married to Parvati, a girl with green eyes, the daughter of one of the goldsmiths on 90 Feet Rd, the principal artery which divides the district in two. An excellent match, because most of the squatters have no confidence in the banks, and, as a result, there's always a roaring trade in gold.

Dharavi expanded in the late forties on swampland, that gradually developed into an illegal rubbish tip. As the tip spread it turned the swamp into a landfill and became a settlement for newcomers to the city in search of a better life.

In sixty years, as the city grew up around it, Dharavi became surprisingly central, but it was always illegal: completely self-built and self-regulated. It was so dense that when they threw the party for Raksha and Parvati's wedding, they had had to dismantle one of the kilns at Kumbharwada, the pottery district, to make room for the band and the dancing. The party came to an end at dawn, then dozens of people set to work to reassemble the furnace quickly, so as not to waste a day's work.

Nothing is wasted in Dharavi, everything has a second, third or fourth life. At times it seems the whole district lives on whatever is discarded by the surrounding city.

After his outburst Praku pauses. It has done us good to talk about it. He knows I understand him and a lot remains to be done. He smiles at me with his irresistible raconteur's expression, urging me to go and tell the whole story to Jockin Arputham, founder and undisputed leader of the NSDF, and the other activists at SPARC.

I am certain we will talk till dawn, chai after chai, chewing over the possible lines of action and how to organize a consciousness-raising campaign. As we walk, Praku keeps up his incessant flow of encouragement. Basically, if we're organized we can't possibly lose. We're just too many for them. However powerful they are, in a democracy they'll have to listen …

I keep my misgivings to myself. Better not damp his enthusiasm. Tomorrow will be another day of struggle for the right to the city. We'll need all the enthusiasm we can muster. ■

MONU
MENTS

FOR

RESI
DENTS

BEGINNINGS

THE SODOMIST CAR

At first, surprised by the hairy tuning of the car, I asked him:
"Are you driving your dog inside?" He replied:
"No, this is because my two bodyguards are so hairy: hairy-bulgairy.

The car of Sodom crashed many minds in Bulgaria, and created
thousands of flat memories, which stocked onto each other became the
seven residential towers of Cherni Vrah. Flats start from the seventh
floor and continue to the twenty-nineth floor.

The Sodom Car enters through a ramp in the basement, the Resident
penetrates the sarcophague in the hairy ground floor – a symbolical act
of architectural sodomism.

CHERNI VRAH : SEX = DEATH

Symmetry was created by mirroring. The Mirror glasss, the mirror walls and floors, sometimes mirror ceilings were frequently used materials in the building.

Mirrors double space. Space is extended to the unendless, reaching to the realms of death.

In the unlimited space, the Resident could unleash his fantasies, which he had in the vast fields of sex technique knowledge. During years of perverted penetrations, he got closer, until he slowly merged with the dead images of himself in the mirror. He petrified in the symmetrical Sex-Death Monument.

THE SUNSET MONUMENT

The crisis came. At this moment of sunset, the Resident was swimming in the pool which is located on the fifth floor with a marvelous view on Vitosha Mountain and the TV tower. Spa and Fitness Centers were next to the pool, to increase his blood circulation and muscle mass or to intensify his erection while observing the sunset.

Training hard, the Resident noticed an inverse effect on his body. It was the crisis impact, causing concave distortions on the mirror walls. Space was getting sparse. A sudden implosion marked the end of Cherni Vrah, covering Sofia with a vacuum of sweat, sperm and black blood.

Seven years later a small sad island showed in the middle of Black Sea. On it, jellyfish, crabs and salt water have formed a wonderful and worth seeing Monument of Sunset.

THE BEAUTY MONUMENT

Under the spa, swimming pool and gym, the fourth floor was the world of beauty. The mirror walls were upgraded with a religious liquify effect, which distorted the dead bodies, the dead faces, the dead eyes looking at them. A world of perfection where the bodies of Resident's friends were just a raw liquid mass to be formed into divine accessories for having fun. The enormous creative power of mirror and liquify operations resulted in an overproductioin of silicone, hair extensions and bottox skin. The beauty sauce was squirting out of the house, petrifying in the daylight as the famous Bulgarian Beauty Monument, which as some tourist kept telling about, it looked like mayonaise.

THE BIRTH OF MODERN BULGARIAN ARCHITECTURE

In these days inverse bodybuilding was very popular among Bulgarian Residents. The head was small, forming the flat triangle end of a trapezoid neck, nurbing with shoulders, which were the beginning of a watermellon monsterbelly. This imposing advanced geometry composition ended with several blobs, which could be perhaps an ass, or legs. The floors of the food court, dealing with these complicated non-euclidian deformation models under intimidating masses of human flesh were located in the third floor.

The Resident, feeding italian slad with mayonaise and even more pure mayonaise collapsed under his dead load, sedimenting on the floor, turning eventually into concrete reinforcement (see the black part of the image). This food court was discovered by archeologists and later known in architectural theory circles as the Bulgarian Organic Phenomenon: Architecture feeding residents and feeding on them simultaneously!

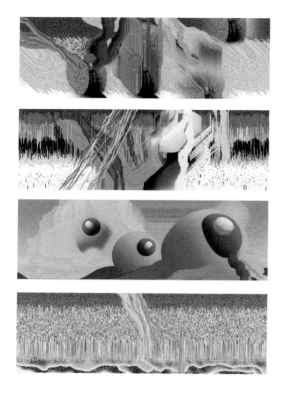

Because Cherni Vrah was pretty scary (angstful) the decorations were made in a very beautiful way, to distract the Resident from possible thinking about something. Most talented bulgarian and foreign masters of decoration were covered with gold and diamonds to create a specific uplifting visual atmosphere in the building. Seven tryptichons for every week day built up the most influential masterpiece, which was situated in the main lobby. Of a particular interest are four of them: one, depicting a gentleman projection of three vaginas, one showing hair extensions in many colors, symbolizing freedom of choice and triumph of individuality, one is dedicated to the genesis of a silicon breast, and one is a sad ocean landscape with the endangered species of sperm whales. These and more interventions of ambient artists, such as the emerging sound curtain of uplifting house beats emphasize the importance of art in buidings today.

ANGSTERS AND RESIDENTS

END 1. THE BULGARIAN ANGSTER

I became a wholly new person. My 3D-thinking was gone because of the flat Mercedes wheel pattern plastic surgery I received on this hot summer day.

Suddenly I was interested in condensed design.

I realized that I was dealing with fear, I became an Angster.

An Angster is an architect gangster dealing with fear, or a senior Angst-dealing youngster, flattened to the concrete by an autobahn prankster. For these Angsters, Angst is the primary building material.

Yes, I started.

As a flat Angster I was in the power of designing flats for the three-dimensional Bulgarian Resident. Instead of concrete cubes, for the project I had to use their condensed form – concrete pixels.

But where was the third dimension? It's lack made me angstful in the office during endless facebook and google earth hours instead of working…

I took the obstruse coincidence as an important design rule. Since the building has 29 floors, and on every floor there are let's say 29 residents, there are 841 residents. They will spend 29 years in the building, which means 841x29= 24389 years. Translated into days it is exactly 8.901.984 days. The second important design rule I took from David Bowie: seven days to live my life and seven ways to die.

The building had to have flats, shops, pool, beauty center, elevators, parking, gardens, security systems and a roof.

These ingredients were assembled to a building – simultaneously a sarcophague, a grave and a monument of residency.

The Resident was embraced by the building as an egyptian pharaon, together with his most valuable belongings, favorite sunglasses, dog and wife.

He had one function in this coffin: to spend his time.

The building's function was to absorb it: a time processing machine it swallowed every hour after hour falling into its groundings, creating layers of time, growing to a ghost time structure.

I created Cherni Vrah – a black hole building, full of time, millions of people hours.

It is a building of life and death. The life of architecture, the death of the Resident.

Twenty nine years waiting to become an Angster, twenty nine layers has the building. Layers of dead life. Every layer consists of millions of pixels, every pixel means an hour.

Pixels picture images of absorbed life, sedimented into layers of memory, petrified into monuments of death. Building of Angst.

END 2. THE BULGARIAN RESIDENT

When I first met the Bulgarian Resident, he didn't speak to me.

Hidden behind the dark glasses of its Mercedes GL, he opened the window. It was a hot summer day around 4.30 p.m. I could feel the air conditioning blowing into my face, making my hair and mind windy.

The Bulgarian Resident had a round shaved face. He was sweating, especially his chin, nose and the hair above his ears. I guess his eyes were morbid, but they were hidden behind dark sunglasses.

The motor of the five-liter Mercedes engine, or his voice were saying something which I couldn't hear.

Something about the crisis.

In the next moment the skin of my face felt the hot surface of the asphalt – the urban Autobahn Cherni Vrah, connecting Sofia with the Vitosha Mountain.

Above me was the fat wheel of the Mercedes rolling. My bones were crashing, my flesh tearing apart.

I stopped thinking, because the wheel of the fat car ironed my head onto the street.

I felt Angst. ∎

The building Cherni Vrah in Sofia (english translation – Black Top) is the first building of the bulgarian architect Iassen Markov. After his study and theoretical work in Stuttgart he was challenged with the design of a real project, w ich has to be built in the Bulgarian capital Sofia. An irony of life – this building has 29 Floors, and Iassen Markov is by this time also 29 years old. Every floor meant one year of Markov's life.

OPEN SPACES

&

LITTLE SISTERS

by Marc Schuilenburg

Technology has been an integral part of our lives for some years now. A new generation of designers and urban development planners use technology for the design of both personal space and large-scale urban areas. Focussing on the personal environment (the car, our house, the office, etc.), we see an impressive migration of computer technology to all kinds of objects designed to make our lives more comfortable and to respond to the needs of the individual. This is called ambient intelligence. Technical devices are invisibly integrated in the walls of our house, in our clothes, our bank cards, or even in our bodies; all of which we do not seem to perceive as intrusive or as a violation of our privacy. Examples are microchips in televisions and microwaves that operate wirelessly and respond to the wink of an eye or a simple hand gesture. Also the 'intelligent' refrigerator, which keeps stock of our groceries and informs the supermarket of our shopping list, is an example of user-friendly intelligence designed to adapt to our preferences and moods. The user does not have to adapt to the technology; the technology adapts to the user.

The magical promise of ambient intelligence is that it is designed to provide service and support. It will heighten our sense of comfort and security. We like that. After all, our time spent queuing in supermarkets can hardly be put into perspective. On average, we spend at least one year of our lives in queues. However, there is more to this issue that meets the eye. For instance, what happens with your intelligent fridge if the profile of your roommate is tagged because he stole a candy bar in a supermarket? And how can we relate to the space between our kitchen and the supermarket? Is it a private or public environment … or something completely different?

In order to elucidate upon this, technology must be viewed in a much broader context. It is not neutral, quite the opposite. Technology covers the way in which our social reality is experienced. It not only leads to a different partitioning of the space in the city, but also contributes to a specific understanding of ourselves.

Capturing the sense of space in the city can prove to be a bit of a challenge, but a bird's-eye view quickly reveals that three 'hard lines' give city life consistency, coherence, and direction. These lines encompass people and have a history of their own. They divide the city and its inhabitants in specific areas. Such strict divisions often have a political-economical basis and are ideologically founded. Once drawn, they produce specific effects and serve a particular purpose. What divisions are we referring to?

Firstly, binary oppositions such as 'city-countryside' and 'nature-culture' come to mind. Long ago these divisions ensured that city dwellers felt protected and sheltered from dangers lying outside the sphere of their influence. Advancing urbanization has weakened both divisions. Other oppositions, however, have taken their place. The distinction 'public-private', for example, which goes back to the French Revolution. At that time two spheres were created in order to convey what was meant by 'life'. The private sphere is where the authorities should not intervene; behind closed doors each individual is entitled to his own desires and beliefs. In the public sphere, however, the individual becomes a citizen who is expected to let public interest prevail over his own desires and beliefs. The public sphere is where you should be protected by the authorities from people who might harm you.

Secondly, we see that the city is divided in ever-expanding circles. This is the second 'hard line'. It starts with the bed, followed by the room, then the house, the street, the neighbourhood, the borough, the city, etc. These 'circular divisions' are ever-expanding and, consequently, so is the environment in which we live and move. Each circle encompasses one or more other circles. The nature of the circle changes as soon as elements of a small circle are absorbed by a larger circle, are coupled with other elements, or simply disappear. The larger the circle, the more complicated the social structure and relations within this inner world.

Thirdly, there are 'linear divisions'. These regard the different periods or phases in our life succeeding each other chronologically: family life, school, army, career, etc. The transitions between these phases is what we refer to as 'growing up'. On the one hand this third line is characterized by the function-specific position of each phase. Every place -school, military camp, work – has its idiosyncrasies, or, in other words, its own physical, social, and symbolic characteristics. On the other hand, each phase is concluded when the next one begins. At school, writes Deleuze in 'Postscript on the Societies of Control', they tell you that you are not at home anymore. At work they tell you: 'You are not at school anymore'. The result of all of this is a succession of phases and spaces in which the individual moves from point to point as if something new could be added to his life constantly.

These three hard lines have been reflected upon and written about considerably. Historical research has shown that each line has its own dynamics, which do not always dovetail with the other two. They often ignore each other; sometimes even turn against each other, but more often they reinforce each other, overlap, or converge in new divisions.

Such historical tracings are valuable in themselves, but they do little justice to the history of a more invisible space through which we move. This 'space' goes beyond the classical dichotomies and modernistic divisions of the urban space: it runs straight across the three divisions described here. We call this invisible space an 'open' or 'medial space'.

The definition of the word 'open' is 'not shut' (doors, gates, etc.), but also 'not covered, naked, clear'. The term expresses a notion of origin. In the words of urbanist Pieter Uyttenhove: 'Each beginning, each origin – birth, Big Bang, awakening, liberation, breakthrough – is a form of opening'. Even though the meaning of the word adapts to the spirit of the times and to the local circumstances, in the world of architecture and urban development it is mainly used to describe publicly accessible space. This is referred to as public space. This is where people can freely meet and exchange ideas.

The character of public space has changed significantly over the past centuries. In the 18th century it encompassed coffee houses and parks which served as public meeting places where differences of opinions were settled and the public opinion was formed. Shopping arcades and publicly accessible libraries symbolized the modern public nature of society in the 19th century. Places referred to as 'mass private properties' are of more recent date. These include shopping centres, amusement parks, sports stadiums, and office parks. Although these areas are usually private property, they undeniably have a public function. They serve as a space where people can build a united world. The same can be seen in the virtual environments of online games such as 'World of Warcraft' and 'Second Life', where eleven to twelve million people gather every day.

In spite of the metamorphoses of public space over the centuries, this space has always been a clear example of the first hard line. The dichotomy 'public-private' has served its purpose quite well for many centuries, but it now seems to be past its prime. If one looks at the changes in the urban landscape with an open mind one will see that, to a degree, public space and private space overlap in various areas. These overlaps are never stable or static. They are not sharply delineated and constantly change their shape, range, and composition due to several causes. Developments such as privatization, globalization, and a decreasing trust in the extent to which urban space can be effected by government policies, for example. The most important reason, however, is rooted in the influence of new technologies (rfid-tags, chips, smart dust, etc.), which cause overlaps not only in the physical and virtual space, but especially in the public and private space. This digital infiltration – described by Peter Sloterdijk as a new phase of the globalization process – not only made the city a part of a transnational dynamic, but has also had an influence on its physical environment. This allows us to be private in a public space and public in a private space.

How does this happen?

Back to the fridge.

In an information-based environment strict divisions such as 'private-public' dissolve. This means that the relation between public and private itself has changed. Separate areas are connected and subsequently fulfil another function in another connection. In other words, delineated space to which access is restricted is absorbed by an 'open' or 'medial space'. This space realizes itself in what it has made disappear. The same technologies used to deliver groceries to our house also bridge the distance between our kitchen and the supermarket. Our house and the shop thus no longer operate as separate entities; instead there is a continuous connection via modern information technologies. Bearing this in mind, can we still maintain that hard lines separate 'inside' and 'outside'? Or should we argue that 'inside' and 'outside' are inextricably intertwined?

The 21th century, the century in which technological media have first comprehensively penetrated our lives, presupposes a new conception of space. Instead of being finite in its boundedness, an open space is flexible and derives its form from the context within which it is contained. It does not have a well-defined content or fixed form. It can be expanded in every direction and is confined only by a horizon that moves as people, goods and information move. Illustrative of such territorial expansion is imprisonment. Electronic supervision, which allows the inmate to serve his prison sentence outside the walls of a prison cell, shifts the prison environment to the inmate's immediate home environment. But also the transition from school to work and home has become diffuse. The factory is no longer the working place you leave behind after working hours. With the rise of immaterial labour it has become customary to take work home, to finish a report in the weekend, and to check e-mails during vacation. At the same time, the working place has changed into a feel-good environment, with cosy coffee corners and comfortable lounge areas; all of this to make your time at work as enjoyable as possible and, maybe, make it feel a little bit like home.

All of this does not mean that you can do whatever you please in an open space. Deleuze writes: 'We don't have to stray into science fiction to find a control mechanism that can fix the position of any element at any given moment – an animal in a game reserve, a man in a business (electronic tagging)'. The introduction of the shops ban order illustrates this. This order is used increasingly by shop owners in large-scale urban areas. One who shops in a shopping area that has such a policy and displays anti-social behaviour may have a shops ban order issued against him for all the shops that support the policy. Steal one candy bar from one particular supermarket and you are faced with a shops ban for all the shops in the city centre. Not only that particular supermarket is off limits; all other shops are as well. Since 2005 over a thousand of such shops ban orders have been issued in cities as The Hague and Rotterdam.

Although the term 'shops ban' suggests that only shops are concerned, theatres, studios and galleries, hotels, banks, restaurants, and even chemists use such ban orders as well. Invisible networks allow these companies to exchange personal details of people who have been issued a ban order (facial features, address, name, etc.). A distinctive type of 'infrastructure' is installed on multiple levels, not only on the scale of global flows of people, goods and information, but also on the scale of streets, shops and homes, all in order to create a sense of security. In other words: information on who is and isn't welcome.

Because of technologies such as 'face-check', CCTV and shared data-bases, these spaces are increasingly taking on a life of their own. In that sense they are not passive shells but rather active processes. Time and time again one is forced to ask oneself the question: am I still permitted access? An open space, therefore, is not a homogeneous or undivided space as if it contained no segments or rifts. After all, it may contain several spaces, like several languages may exist within a language. Admittedly, an open space is not restricted by the three hard lines described here, but access can be partially restricted for certain people. A cooperative environment thus becomes an opposing environment, as in the case of the shops ban order.

The shops ban order can be distinguished from the detailed forms of discipline, as Michel Foucault described them in his classic book Discipline and Punish. This type of security technique is not aimed at normalization through a process of enclosure which re-establishes the status quo. Access may be denied somewhere else in the Netherlands as well. In contrast to a 'punishment mentality', in which a person is punished because he has committed a wrongful act in the past, this future-oriented approach is based on a 'precaution mentality', that is associated with the potential for loss, harm, injury or destruction. Its purpose is to make the future more certain. Therefore, this technique is no longer meant to keep one inside a closed space, but is installed in order to create a open space, which allows 'free' movement, while being perfectly controlled. This is also a key theme in the film Minority Report in which technical devices identify certain people as possible perpetrators before they have actually committed a crime.

All sorts of invisible 'open' or 'medial spaces' come into being in our urban landscape. They unmake spatial boundaries of a given entity, such as the city, and create new assemblages in which people 'act and speak' and are reassembled together. However, what has received little attention is the fact that also a different self-consciousness is created in these spaces. So, if the distance is bridged between 'house and shop', 'prison and home' and 'work and school' in the face of the rise of a precaution society, what will become of the homo clausus? What will capture the state of mind of a contemporary individual? Would the person, who slowly but surely hands over the most intimate details of his human existence in order to sustain the flow, not best be characterized as a homo transparantus?

The characterization of a homo transparantus marks those persons who have 'revealed themselves'. Once identified, they can be continuously monitored and followed through different technologies and the integration of computer systems and databases. At the same time, these technologies are continuously mapping the 'factors of risk' of an individual person. Our body has become pure information. We no longer find ourselves dealing with a universal or general category of mankind. We have become informants on ourselves. We are 'dividuals': physically embodied human subjects that are endlessly divisible and reducible to data representations via technologies of control, like computer-based systems. The implications are that uncertain elements or 'risk-persons' are set apart and become 'neutralized'.

This form of precaution leads to a great deal of speculation about whether we have entered George Orwell's world of 'Big Brother is watching you'. Such a dystopian view, however, has not been realized the way George Orwell imagined. The Big Brother metaphor suggests that everything is watched and observed from one single point. In our cities, however, all kinds of identity control practices are proliferating in everyday life. A whole variety of practices – tax offices, supermarkets, banks, neighbourhoods, hospitals, and insurance companies – has been set up to make it possible for people to anonymously report their neighbours on issues varying from social benefit fraud to domestic violence, from suspicious behaviour to an actual crime being committed.

This is what Orwell seems to have overlooked when he described the role of technology in his novel 1984. Instead of Big Brother, it is now better to speak of Little Sisters. ∎

Recommended readings:

De Jong, A. & M. Schuilenburg (2007), Mediapolis. Popular Culture and the City, Rotterdam: 010-Publishers.

Deleuze, G. (1995), Postscript on the Societies of Control, in: Negotiations 1972–1990, New York: Columbia University Press, p. 172–182.

Romein, E. & M. Schuilenburg (2008), Are you on the fast track? The rise of surveillant assemblages in a post-industrial age, in: Architectural Theory Review, vol. 13, no. 3, p. 337–348.

Uyttenhove, P. (2006), 'De open stad', in: M. Dings (red.) De stad, Rotterdam: Uitgeverij 010, p. 263–273.

MARC SCHUILENBURG

POST

**A SHORT HISTORY OF
THE POST-CONDITION
IN ARCHITECTURE**

-MODERN
STRUCTURA
-CRITICAL
POLITICAL

by Ole W. Fischer

I. MODERN, POST-MODERN, POST-POST-...?

Post-modern architecture started on March 16, 1972, precisely at 3 p.m. This happened with the implosion of the first unit of the Pruitt-Igoe housing complex, as displayed on American TV. Live.

This was architecture's promise for the emergence of a new human – fallen to dust. The rationality of the architect's plan regarding the idea of a rational, democratic, egalitarian mass society – turned into a nightmare. The humanitarian goal of satisfying, with limited resources, a maximum of users by using industrial construction methods, separation of functions, and the search for an optimal (that is, minimal and standardized) requirement of space – abandoned by the people. The built representation of the contemporary premise of utilitarian thought, administered organization and efficient division of labor – falsified once and for all. The utopian (and educational) project of modernity – blown away with dynamite.

At least that is one of post-modernity's founding myths: we shall believe in some kind of a revolutionary event, like the storming of the Bastille. One era sold out, ended, to give way to something new. However, this 'other' seemed difficult to picture: the projects of Western thought (Enlightenment, Liberalism, Nationalism, Communism) were unmasked as 'grand narrations' and criticized as totalitarian systems. Instead of guiding principles or universalizing concepts post-modern theory now enhanced the open, relative, and pluralistic. The place of mass society, industrial conveyor belt and standardization was taken by individualism, service sector and customization.

In general, the cultural accent shifted from originality, invention and production to citation, estrangement (irony), and mediation. Not for nothing semiotics became the key concept of the time and the analysis of texts and discourses dominate the humanities.

Yet, while modernity defined itself via the differentiation from the past (the nineteenth century), the various currents of post-modern thinking agreed on little much except the idea that modernity had come to an end and had been replaced by something else: that very post-modernity.

Significantly, one of the key battles of the post-modern debate took place in architecture: post-war modernism gained a bad reputation and was attacked from a variegated enmity as example of technocracy and mis-guided development. As there was a clear-cut delineation from modernity (or modernism?), there were heterogeneous alternatives proposed, such as strategies arisen from pop-art, a critical or affirmative exposure to consu-merism, the call for participation of the observer (either directly via advo-cacy planning or indirectly via semiotic layers of meaning), researches into context, structure and typology, or into image, analogy and memory, or, last but not least, neo-historicism.

This all seems a well known story, but it is against these two large cur-rents of the twentieth century that we might inquire after the status quo of today: is it adequate to describe contemporary Western societies with terms such as post-structural, post-Fordist, or post-modern, depending on whether we address their current philosophical, economic or cultural condition?

This raises some doubts, although the search for a term mapping the contemporary situation has not delivered a convincing alternative.

As compared to the 1960s and 1970s massive changes can be felt. However, it is not so obvious if and how the social, economic, political and technical transformations affect cultural practices. In architecture, for exam-ple, 'post-modern' became a stylistic etiquette for the semiotic experiments of the seventies and eighties, which were soon replaced by 'deconstruc-tion', 'neo-modern' and 'minimalism' – although these can be read in continuity of a linguistic-pluralistic post-modern culture, where 'modern' became only one of many available (historic) styles.

II. CAPITALISM, NEO-CAPITALISM, POST-CAPITALISM?

Capitalism is dead. Long live capitalism!

In 1969 the radical architects group Archizoom exhibited 'No-Stop City'. Modeled after car parks and shopping centers, the singular architectural object no longer exists. In what has been interpreted as a fundamental critique of modernist rationalism and a plea for popular culture and a design lifestyle, architecture evaporated into isotropic megastructures, into endless, repetitive interiors where the only spatial feature left is building technology. Architecture is replaced by planning, presented as scientific, integrated control that pretends to organize economic and social development in space.

But this is just an exaggeration of the architectural and urbanistic trends of the 1960s, a radicalization – not for its own end, but to provoke the transgression of the system into revolutionary events and finally lead to the emergence of 'new wild realities'.

Avoiding the traditional individual signature of the master architect, Archizoom Associati was formed in Florence in 1966 as a corporate group under a brand name. In their work, they put project and process in place of refined architectonic objects, and integrated affirmative graphic design as well as technologic progress.

However, in contrast to American corporate architecture and the pop- and technophile English group Archigram – to which Archizoom ironically refers – these projects have to be read as a critical commentary on capitalist society. Based on the Italian actionist, neo-Marxian operaista movement, they take the concept of 'society as factory' and apply it to architecture: unlike the shiny smooth surfaces and technologic perfection of corporate late modernism, 'No-Stop City' displays the processual, systemic and totalistic nature of post-war neo-capitalism.

The 'neo' in neo-capitalism derives from the lessons learnt during the Great Depression of the 1930s: Keynes' argument for international agreements, strong state, demand-driven, countercyclical economic policy and new instruments of control were soon 'internalized' by business practice.

The American New Deal and wartime economy enforced new means of planning, control and participation that kicked off the evolution of (trans-) national companies, corporate business and mass consumption. Together with improvements in production, financing, marketing and distribution these lead to an update of capitalist societies. In Western Europe, the incorporation of socialist claims undermined the old antagonism between capitalists and laborers and paved the way for economic recovery of the 1950s and 1960s.

However, the integration of traditional labor organizations (parties, unions) into institutionalized democratic politics and liberal economy rendered alternatives to the hegemonic social model impossible: a well-tempered atrium of corporate offices and shopping malls with no exit.

Today, the experimental, utopian and radical architecture of the 1960s enjoys great popularity amongst architects. However, this happens against a changed socio-economic background, as neo-capitalist interdependence of state, unions, banks and corporations have disintegrated.

The disappearance of the working class in favor of 'classless' consumers and jobholders in Western societies matches the shift from 'use value' to 'exchange value' of contemporary products: by purchasing sneakers, lemonade or mobile phones we do not get an object, but a lifestyle. Culture and art are as easily consumable as resistance and underground.

On the other hand, state interventions referring (often wrongly) to Keynes have proven their own risk sensitivity and went out of fashion with neoliberal administrations taking office in the eighties, before deregulation, privatization and dismantling the welfare state became the standard repertoire of Western politics in the nineties. And countries of the 'second' and 'third world' have had to deal with much more dramatic shifts of their political, economic and social order.

Seen retrospectively, neo-capitalism appears to be a byproduct of the cold war, which means that the fall of the wall also had its effects in the West, where there still isn't an adequate term to describe the notion of 'post-communism'.

Under the banner of globalization, supposedly 'victorious' capitalism has since demonstrated its crisis-laden evolution, as well as its ability to integrate excluded territories and populations into its system of exploitation.

If the recent financial crisis adds another chapter to capitalist evolution between boom and crash, or if it will structurally change the system (like neo-capitalism), or even mark the transition to another – something like post-capitalism – remains to be seen, but it does leave some space for speculation, hope and action.

III. STRUCTURAL, POST-STRUCTURAL, POST-CONTEMPORARY?

What ever happened to deconstruction?
When on June 23, 1988 the New York MoMA put 'Deconstructivist Architecture' on show, the triumph of 'critical' architecture seemed perfect, if merely within academia.

Yet, a few years later, this movement had left the international architectural discourse almost unrecognized, after having boosted its protagonists (Koolhaas, Gehry, Eisenman, Hadid, Libeskind, Coop Himmelb(l)au, Tschumi) into the favorite circle of the global star system. In the new context, their 'signature buildings' give evidence of a post-structuralist reading strategy turned into architectural style.

After '68, the project to 'criticize' the 'discipline' of architecture from within was launched as a double rejection against semiotic post-modernism as well as techno-functional late modernism. In order to enable a 'critical' practice within the prevailing social order of capitalism and mass consumer culture, architecture had to be rethought, like minimal and conceptual art, as autonomous and abstract design. Some architects considered that the vocabulary of the 'heroic' modern architecture of the 1920s – and especially Russian Constructivism – was not yet exhausted and could feed a 'neo-avantgarde'. With the help of linguistic theories, such neo-avantgarde thus continued the formal language of modernism.

But the latter's social program was left behind.

Soon they established 'critical' characteristics such as post-functional formalism, abstract manipulation of geometric elements, display of architectonic conventions etc. Their projects – often restricted to paper – were accompanied by elaborated theoretic texts that made references to (post-) structural authors. Time after time 'critical' architects claimed a disjunction, decomposition, deconstruction or transgression of architecture, or explained verbosely its problematization, resistance and silence.

Despite the change from structuralist to post-structuralist references in a constant battle for fashionable theories, the design strategies remained similar over time. Even after the introduction of digital technologies, instead of unmasking the established power relations (which architecture and urbanism tend to glorify), instead of uncovering the construction of the discipline (of architecture and planning), instead of questioning the essential categories of thinking, speaking and writing (about architecture) the outcome of (post-)structuralism got reduced to form finding.

Over the last decade there has been a return to more classic disciplinary positions, rendering the architect either as pragmatic service provider or as ingenious artist. Or both: this is the position of Frank Gehry, despite all formal similarity to deconstructivism.
Ironically, there is a coincidence of decomposition with extravagance, of critique of representation with media-architecture, of the death of the author with the birth of the icon.

As a result, architecture is now 'contemporary'.
Many of its themes and topics such as convex-concave shapes, fluid surfaces, amorphous seamlessness, processuality, dynamism, variability and the whole attempt to integrate temporality into architectural design cannot be ascribed to digital technology alone.
For sure, CAD, Photoshop and animation have their share in the dematerialization and virtualization of architecture. Hence the frequent reference to Deleuze. But there is an alternative genealogy, beyond IT and French philosophy, that is rarely reflected by its protagonists and interpreters: spatial liquidity, transformation and morphing celebrate the dissolution of social, political and economic boarders, and illustrate the deregulated flow of humans, goods and capital around the globe.
Diagram, process, and parametric architecture say more about capitalist ideologies of planning and control, about human-machine-systems (cybernetics) and its update by system theories than about liberating possibilities of transgression and affect.
As such, contemporary architecture embellishes the tendency of total integration into a global system of exploitation.

If contemporaneity is something like the ultimate modernist legacy, then the concept of post-contemporary promises to surpass architecture's obsession to express the moment (Zeitgeist).

However, watch your step and be aware of the historic trap: the 'contemporary' is a synonym for the post-war phase in music and art. At one point some critics must have thought that there had to be something after the contemporary.

In other words: we have never been more modern.

IV. CRITICAL, POST-CRITICAL, NEO-PRAGMATIC

Where is architecture after 9/11?

Even within American academia, 'critical' architecture has met with discontent.

Under the name of 'post-criticality' a group of younger theoreticians tries to emancipate from their intellectual godfathers. They propagate 'projective' architecture as an alternative, one that relates to the predominance of architectural design (projects) – and practice in general – over theoretic thinking. 'Projective' also resonates with a future-oriented perspective of the architect, referring to the literal meaning of foreseeing, and this goes along with rejecting the 'critical' instruments of negation and resistance, since they always carry a regressive trait.

Finally, 'projection' borrows from psychology, meaning the transfer of inner, subjective feelings onto outer objects. This connects the 'post-critical' perspective to perception, mood and the immersive atmosphere of the architectural interventions and environments.

Even if this critique of established academic 'critical' architecture – and its caricature of the linguistic post-structural discourse mechanism – seems refreshing, the trouble lies in its fixation on the American debate.

By overestimating the importance of some 'critical' authors, the 'post-criticals' claim the futility of any critical practice in contemporary architecture. They answer the question of the architectural design transformative social power with vaguely quoting the creation of 'alternative life-styles'.

As such, other critical approaches, such as participatory design, critical regionalism, or critical realism with its focus on the everyday are not taken into consideration. Not to speak of political or actionist strategies. Rather, we witness again the curse of reductive dialectics, where thesis is answered by anti-thesis, and one theory by the model of the 'post-', that postulates nothing else but a binary negation, instead of proposing a real alternative.

It might be more than a coincidence that the 'post-critical' entered the scene after 2001, parallel to political revisionism and the 'war against terrorism'.

Already in the early 1990s some voices tried to challenge 'critical' theory by demanding a positive relationship to the market and American popular culture, respectively denouncing abstraction, resistance and intellectual criticism as elitist Eurocentrism.

The implicit suspicion of anti-Americanism avails itself of the neo-pragmatist school of thought, as well as of its historical context: the fall of the wall in 1989/90 seemed to falsify the (neo-) Marxist heritage of all 'critical' theories.

With their primacy of practice and their notion of a liberal, democratic and egalitarian consumer society, the 'post-critical' authors of today tie in with older post-modernist theories, such as the affirmative reading of Las Vegas by Venturi & Scott Brown or the appraisal of Disneyland as model for new urban public space by Charles Moore.

In this sense, the contemporary 'projective' seems much less 'post-critical' than merely 'pre-critical'.

V. LA RECHERCHE DU THÉORIE PERDU, OR: THE PRACTICE OF THEORY AND THEORY OF PRACTICE

What is 'left'?

Architecture has a difficult relationship to society, which resurfaces as the old question of content and form.

Almost every design project comments on society, because it provokes deviance from the existing and opens a window of possibilities.

This foreseeing (projective?) aspect of architectural design is initially independent of the formal style or expression chosen. But the question of meaning immediately recurs, with its political, historical or ideological inscriptions.

Contrary to classical notions of semiotics, architecture does not 'speak', but its forms are neither 'free' nor 'innocent', since observers and users constantly interpret them against the background of their knowledge and memory. The future oriented vector of design contains a fundamental 'critical' potential by challenging the existing and initiating change.

However, the success of capitalism relies on its faculty to integrate critique, resistance and negation by turning them into 'products'. Or rather: capitalism lives on the promise of novelty and innovation, on the appearance of permanent change. Fashion answers perfectly this demand for constant renewal without touching the existing societal relations.

Therefore, architecture faces a twofold problem: as it is, as a complex, expensive and permanent cultural product, built by order of the elites, it makes it difficult to be more than the embodiment of dominant values.

But under capitalism the innovative, transformative and revolutionary qualities are cashed in as trademark and fashion.

So where is room left for critical practice in contemporary architecture? The retreat into architecture's interiority, into linguistic structure, into autonomous typology, or into geometrical manipulation ends in formalist games. The most recent of these goes in digital disguise by the name of parametric design.

But architecture cannot escape societal relations. Even if unrecognized, these relations force their way back into architecture, as demonstrated by the excursus to the contemporary notions of networks, flows and processes as exemplification and manifestation of global capitalism.

Yet, there seems to be a recent change in articulating architecture's borders, thresholds, envelopes and (solidified) surfaces, which might supply a new want for security and stability or might as well refer to the sustainable debate, which addresses certificates, threshold values, evaluation, performance, etc.

This should not be misunderstood as a plea for sociologic architecture or instrumental politics.

The totalitarian force enclosed in utopian urban projects – already visible in Plato's Politeia and Thomas More's Utopia – has not been averted. And the divergence between humanitarian intentions and the inhuman results pervades the architectural history of the twentieth century.

This is seldom the fault of architecture or planning alone, but of politics, as for example, is the case with the social segregation, dilapidation and hopelessness in the French grande ensembles.

Today, however, the omniscient pose of the modernist master is as inappropriate as the cultish post-modern star architect and his trademark designs.

On the contrary, we need alternative approaches, office structures and practices, where the internal 'criticality' (of architecture) is not mistaken for social or cultural critique.

Choosing a project or client is more relevant than a style. Yet, even sociologically informed design – applying participatory models and ope-rating with flexible, negotiable spaces – can be instrumentalized.

In this sense, the intention to democratize the working environment, to smooth the workflow and increase social interaction might initiate a new stage of reification, as the Bürolandschaft (office landscape) by the Schnelle brothers exemplified in the 1960s by appearing as a social-democratic, emancipatory reform model with cybernetic inspirations.

The retreat of critical architecture into the harbor of the arts does not promise salvation either. Firstly, the art market today has become an example par excellence of a highly volatile exchange. This is why economists analyze it as model for stocks.

Secondly, architecture buys into art by eliminating use, habituation and haptics, which is the political space of the everyday.

More importantly, architecture pursued as pure art falls back on the sacral and cultic. Or into autonomist formalism, whose gesture of negation against commerce and kitsch has worn off.

Projects in the institutional frame of museums, galleries and academia, on the other hand, offer a potential space for critical interventions. An architectural project under the umbrella of the arts might develop a stronger political and social effect than traditional design practice.

However, for the discipline at large, the integration of architecture into the arts would deprive it from its singular relation to life, which has to do with connecting different disciplines, practices and discourses into one singular, material artifact at a precise place.

Similarly, the retreat of critical architectural practice into history and theory, as Manfredo Tafuri had hoped for after '68, has lost much of its glamour. Even worse, his plea for a separation of theory and practice has lead to their alienation. Distancing theory from practice and production did not result in a more 'critical' approach to architecture and its cultural, social and political context, but rather a more ignorant one. Or a more servile one.

Since American 'criticality' was legitimized with Tafuri's writings, the critique of the critique stroked back onto the historian from Venice.

We should then ask for more: a skillful criticism of a building that is able to name what makes the design solution exemplary. Or a critical interrogation of the discipline on the background of the social and political conditions: because the freedom of architectural design has to be understood as contingent, that means, as relative and limited by clients, regulations, technique, builders, etc. – not to mention its capillary connections to power and capital.

But theory is more than description and analysis: it has to regain an active role in practice by locating alternative fields for action, by hypothesizing new developments and initiating critical design strategies.

It has to get out of the intellectual ghetto and back to action.

It has to be political in the old sense of addressing the citizens.

If post-contemporary architecture is about redefining a plausible relationship between the social and the formal, then it is in need of a critical practice as much as of a practical theory.

So, let's work. ∎

SYMPTO MATIC

BEYOND THE ROMANTIC

VALUES

by Markus Miessen

The stateless artist and political activist Gustav Metzger once said: "I relate my approach to homeopathy, which puts poison in the system in order to generate energy to defeat the weakness." Sometimes, one could argue, in order for democracy to emerge, democracy itself has to be avoided at all cost. In order to make decisions within any given collaborative structure, network or institution, conflicts can ultimately only be overcome if someone assumes responsibility.

In this context, let us imagine a post-consensual practice, one that is no longer reliant on the often ill-defined modes of operating from within consensus-driven parties or existing political constructs, but instead formulate a necessity to undo the innocence of participation.

The idyllic romanticism of consensus is probably best described through the Dutch Polder model. This model for rebuilding Holland is based on the assumption that something is only 'good' if it benefits the country – based on a general consensus. Such consensus at the core of the state means that everything will be dealt with in terms of pragmatics. The kiss of death of the establishment. Let us not forget: in populist politics, participation is simply and foremost a symbolic gesture. And interestingly, in this setting, if you subtract consensus from participation, you end up with manipulation. England's New Labour movement under Tony Blair notoriously outsourced any kind of supposedly critical decision-making in order to not be held responsible in the end. But why pretend that everyone should always be included in the process? In order to be democratic, you have to be involved. Yes. But you also need to be committed. Assuming responsibility needs to go beyond the current default of using participation as a tool for political legitimization. Realities will hardly change as a result of a reactive drive – let us imagine an ambition beyond absorption and become projective.

We are currently experiencing a point of transition within participatory practices: within politics, within the Left, within spatial practices and –

foremost – within architecture as its visible and most clearly defined product. Participation, both historically and in terms of political agency, is often being read through romantic notions of negotiation, inclusion and democratic decision-making. However, it is precisely this often-unquestioned mode of inclusion being used by populist politicians as a mode of campaigning for retail politics. Hence, it does not produce critical results as criticality is being challenged by the conception of majority. Let us instead imagine a conflictual reading of participation as a mode of practice, one that opposes the brainwave of the democratic facilitator: one that has to assume, at times, non-physical violence and singular decision-making in order to produce frameworks for change.

As a next step, let us challenge the idea that – in general – people have good intentions. Conventional models of participation are based on inclusion. They assume that inclusion goes hand in hand with a standard that is the democratic principle of everyone's voice having an equal weight within egalitarian society. Usually, the simple fact that one proposes a structure or situation in which this bottom-up inclusion is being promoted, the political actor or agency proposing it will be most likely be understood as a 'good-doer', social actor or even philanthropist. Interestingly, the model of the 'curator', for example, is essentially based on the practice of making decisions and therefore eliminating choice rather than boosting plurality by inclusion. In the face of permanent crisis, both the Left and the Right have celebrated participation as the saviour from all evil, an unquestioned form of soft politics. But can we employ the idea of crisis to question our deepest assumptions? Should we rethink our values and devise new principles for action?

Let us imagine a conception of participation as a way to enter politics – proactively and consciously forcing us into existing power-relations by intent – as opposed to a politically motivated model of participation, which tends to propose to let others contribute to the decision-making process. The latter, we might think, is habitually stirred by the craving for political legitimization. The former may be of interest not out of disbelief of democratic principles per se, but out of sheer interest in critical and productive change.

One could argue that this model includes a certain opportunism. Yes and no. It challenges the widespread default that majority equals judiciousness, while arguing for a pro-active citizenship in which the individual outsider to a given inbred political structure can become a driving force for change: forcefully entering an existing discourse rather than opening it up to the floor. Remaining within the arena of 'the democratic', let us instead bastardize participation into a form of non-democratic practice, an opportunistic model of interventionism, in which interference is made possible due to the fact that one is no longer following existing protocols of internalized political struggle. Such model, we could then argue, is that of Crossbench Practice.

Let us imagine this as an ongoing project. Let us begin now. As a first step, let us attempt to open up a new language of practice, a field of operation rather than confronting an existing one. Within this frame, let us unleash a series of experiments that shall be conducted over time. Each of those experiments shall be directed towards the undoing of the innocence of participation. Some of them may be text-based, others set up as projects, yet again others as urban interventions or institutional models – small-scale local test-grounds for change.

Each one of those projects to come shall be understood as particles within a galactic model, in which planets are circulating around an empty void. This void may be loaded with a model for practice by the end of the experiment. The model may present and open questions neither hierarchically organized nor in a field, but in form of a galaxy: a relational model that challenges political romanticism in order to open up the potentiality for a more diffused form of work.

Within a series of case studies conducted over the past years, this pamphlet is the third component within a tripartheid structure that attempts to question existing notions of participatory practice, resulting from increasing gradients of political disillusionment: the first one simply questioned it (Did Someone Say Participate? An Atlas of Spatial Practice[1]). The second one kicked it (The Violence of Participation[2]). The third one, which may be titled Crossbench Practice, will eventually propose an alternative.

What will be presented as a project in question is a theory of how to participate from outside existing power-structures – rather than inside-out. Where traditionally participation is understood as a bottom-up practice, the one being presented here sidesteps the democratic invitation process and enters the conversation mid-level, from the side, so to speak, exposing the often concealed dead end of participation.

What is/are the alternative(s) to conventional confrontation, based on the nostalgic notion of the barricade? How can one propose an alternative practice engaging in spatial projects dealing with social and political realities? What could such polyphonic practice potentially be? What is the mode of relevance of such work and does it always necessitate in 'urgent relevance'? But let us not concentrate too much on the urgent as we might forget about the important.

A substantiated mode of 'scattered practice' could put life as practice into a format that uses as a starting point the will to act without mandate. Such self-initiated practice outside of those existing economies in which there is a clear distinction between client and service provider may enter and in fact produce an alien discourse or field of knowledge productively.

Spatial planning is often considered as the management of spatial conflicts. The city – and, indeed, the progressive institution – exist as social and spatial conflict zones, renegotiating their limits through constant transformation. To deal with conflicts, critical decision-making must evolve. Such decision-making is often pre-supposed as a process whose ultimate goal is that of consensus. Opposing the politics of consensus, critical spatial practice shall foster micro-political participation in the production of space and ask the question of how one can contribute to alien fields of knowledge, professions or discourses from the point of view of 'space'. Like the original meaning of the Latin word conflictus (fight), spatial con-flicts represents a clash of interests in using space. Spatial planning is often considered as the management of spatial conflicts. But who should do what, when and how? The future spatial practitioner could arguably be understood as an outsider who – instead of trying to set up or sustain common denominators of consensus – enters existing situations or projects by deliberately instigating conflicts between often-delineated fields of knowledge.

To enquire the role of the architect and the role of the contemporary institution, existing models of participation may be in need of revision, both in terms of the culture of consensus and the ethos of compromise. We may detect a need for actors operating from outside existing networks of exper-tise, leaving behind circles of common proficiency attempting to overlap with other post-disciplinary realities. Instead of aiming for synchronization, such model could be based on participation through critical distance and the conscious implementation of zones of conflict. Within such zones, one could imagine the dismantling of existing situations for the benefit of being able to strategically isolate components that could be (mis)used to stir friction. Such practice would help to understand the effects of political, economic, and social design-components on space. Using the architect's expertise of mapping out fields of conflict, we may generate an archipelago of questions that seek to uncover the relevance of spatial and architectural expertise and how, in the remit of institutions, they can generate an alter-native knowledge production.

Rather than delivering a recipe, we may lay out a field of potential departures that might allow us to understand what and how an architect can contribute to the questions at hand, tracing some of the above elements in order to create a selective and operational view. What makes an architect's approach to investigating a situation different from the default approaches of other fields of knowledge? What is the value of an Uninvited Outsider, a Crossbench Practitioner that is juxtaposed to a classical, market-driven consultancy methodology? Why the hell talk to architects in the first place?

Let us try to read the phenomenon of participation through a chain of variable spectacles, depending on the respective and diversified angles of observation. In regards to political science, the core relevant arguments of Chantal Mouffe and Antonio Gramsci may be put in the context of and into conflict with the UK's New Labour model or indeed the even more consensus driven Dutch Polder model. Within the larger remit of late 20th century philosophy, the writings of Jacques Rancière and Edward Said could be examined, most specifically Representations of the Intellectual[3]. Concerning spatial practices, the practice of soft thinking in architecture could be read through Keller Easterling or Eyal Weizman. We can draw from texts by Marius Babias and Dieter Lesage to open up the field of critical discourse within contemporary artistic practices as well as thoughts about the notion of collaboration by Florian Schneider. German politician Joschka Fischer's biography may be hijacked in order to produce a case study to illustrate the intricacies of Gramsci's slow march through the institutions. Over the course of his controversial career, Fischer evolved from an archetypal 1960s radical into a smart political insider. Yet, arguably, his biography exemplifies the difficulties of the Gramscian Left and its embedded romanticism regarding notions of protest. While most protagonists of the 1960s and '70s have fully acclimatized themselves to cultural gentrification, purposefully institutionalized their biographies, and settled into middle- and upper-class lifestyles, they accuse younger generations of being consensus-driven and no longer critically aware. To effect 'revolutionary' change, Gramsci proposed a "long march through the institutions", by which he meant the appropriation of cultural institutions at large (media, academies, and theaters). He believed that these very institutions needed to be appropriated in order to change culture at large. In most cases, however, the results of this slow takeover ended up in conventional frameworks, established protocols and default consensus practice.

Let us hope that this imaginary methodology will constitute evidence for the question at hand. The resulting material may constitute neither a historic survey nor a report from the front lines of activism, but – at best – a self-generated concoction of diversified support-structures to demystify romanticized participatory practices: a confined voice that allows us to differentiate the existing discourse further while stimulating an already heated debate. In fact, this may not even be a methodology but a nightmare. A nightmare with a productive end. It may neither be approved by academics nor possibly will it be read by commuters on the train. It will probably not enter the canon of history or be available in a public library. And precisely there may lie the transition-point of opportunity: to produce a condition of politics by considering things before they exist – to speculate with force.

The perhaps autocratic model of participation that I will put up for discussion should not be understood as a blueprint for practice, but a model of departure. It may start to create the necessary friction in order to both stir debate and move forward practice. If there was only a single objective of this experiment, it may be to develop a common understanding and starting point as to where we can start to disagree from: a theory of how to participate – without squinting at constituencies or voters, but instigating critical debate and – at best – change. There may be two arguments here, one polemical and the other conceptually constructive, both stirred by pragmatic optimism. At times, developed through concrete situations and projects, which Simon Critchley would call 'situated universality'.[4] ∎

This text is based on thoughts that are currently producing Crossbench Praxis (forthcoming, Sternberg Press, 2009).

1   Miessen, Markus and Shumon Basar (eds.), Did Someone Say Participate,
    An Atlas of Spatial Practice, Cambridge (MA): The MIT Press, 2006

2   Miessen, Markus (ed), The Violence of Participation, Berlin & New York: Sternberg Press, 2007

3   Said, Edward, Representations of the Intellectual (The 1993 Reith Lectures),
    New York: Random House, 1996

4   Critchley, Simon, Indefinetely Demanding: Ethics of Commitment, Politics of Resistance,
    London: Verso, 2007, p. 42

MARKUS MIESSEN

THE CITY SEEKERS

WEDNESDAY 11 P.M. **ZHU YU**

During the first half of the session Yu talks about being the doorman of Block 6 at Felicity, 'The Happy Block' as it is branded by the real-estate developers.

Felicity is a large housing development located on the South side of the Central Business District. He doesn't understand why so many foreigners have decided to live in this part of the city and has difficulties distinguishing one foreigner from the other. Can I prescribe pills to solve his problem?

Zhu is still bothered by the CCTV building and repeatedly says: "They shouldn't have build it, it is a waste of architecture."

In the second half he explains how he recently got accepted as a member of 'the Group'. He refuses to tell me their real name. I pressure him. To no effect.

It seems that 'the Group' gathers every evening at dusk on a construction site. The members wander around and write down literary texts about the experience.

Someone told Zhu Yu that drugs were involved. Zhu Yu denies to use during these trips. I can't trust him. The meetings culminate with the reading of all the texts; they are presented in front of the concrete skeletons, under flyovers, or near shopping malls.

By the end of the session he asks me not to salute him when I enter Felicity. He knows I live on the other side of the city.

MONDAY 4 A.M. FEI FEI

I notice that Fei Fei's perception of the world is affected by a severe form of architectural amnesia.

I ask her if she thinks it is better that we meet at her place next time.

"I enjoy the traffic jams. They're so slow", she replies.

Fei Fei constantly looks at the built environment as if it is the first time she sees it. In this perpetual state of architectural astonishment she believes that she and the surrounding space are connected in many ways, as within a very complex system. The city would be more meaningful if she realized how disconnected she is from her environment.

The Steinway grand piano finally arrived. In pink, as she requested.

TUESDAY 7 P.M. QANG WU

Wu just wants to talk. I can send him the analysis via email.

I try to listen but I get sidetracked and ponder the question if the city would still have a future if from one day to the other it would be forbidden to photograph the urban setting? Similar to shops where it is forbidden to take pictures of luxury goods (product espionage, intellectual property protection), one can imagine that in the near future, to protect the architect's creativity, it will be forbidden to take pictures of buildings and cities.

SUNDAY 4 P.M. ZHANGWEI BU

We continue our previous conversation and Bu tells me about the train of thoughts that developed in his head during the past week: "As an architect you know your time has come when your employees are getting more famous than you do. Therefore one of the most important tasks of an architect is to keep his employees both ignorant and on top of the times."

I ask for an explanation, wanting to understand the how and what of his reasoning.

Bu is convinced that his staff should know what is going on in the profession, but shouldn't be aware of the mechanisms that stir the course of architecture. "They should know how to design a building, but should be unaware of how to make them, how to move from plan and section to volume and space."

He has Architecture Magazine with him to make his point and page by page he explains his influence on the profession. His ideas are copied and duplicated, starting a life of their own.

He calls this "rather disappointing."

"You know what the problem is? Everybody is working too hard in this profession. Architecture, after all, is not about working hard and intense, but to give the impression you do so. One simply can't tell the masses that architecture is easy. But I can see the difference."

Bu is more talkative than before. I start worrying about him and advice him not to talk to journalists for a while. He also should avoid the exclusive clubs where he spends his nights.

TUESDAY 2 P.M. **MAU HUBEI**

Hubei tells me he prefers to be called 'Bruce'.

Since last week his friends and professional contacts know him by that name. I tell him I didn't check his status updates lately. Mau Bruce it will be.

We quarrel for half an hour about Bigness.

I end the session with my notorious Vance Packard argument on Bigness: "Stratification (formalized inequality of rank) is becoming built-in as almost every sector of our increasingly bureaucratized society moves towards bigness: Big business, Big Government, Big Labour, Big Education. Bigness is one of the really major factors altering our class system."

"Published in 1959", I say, "and nothing changed since then. The status seekers have hardly evolved."

He says it is hard to believe in Bigness before Koolhaas.

We don't schedule a next meeting.

WEDNESDAY 9 P.M. **NANBIAN QIAO**

Qiao's behaviour starts worrying me.

For the second week in a row she only talks about the conflict with her cleaning lady.

"She is a proletarian and refuses to use the French cleaning products to clean the faucets in the bathroom. I don't know anymore how to talk with her. Even the other day she said she preferred cleaning light wood over dark wood. And she knows that my carpenter is one of the few people I trust."

I suggest that she fires her, upon which she pulls the 'friend of the family' card.

For the remainder of the session she gets lost in musing about her contemporary apartment, her interior designers, the paintings she commissioned in the Dafen Art Village and the antiques she recently bought. I laugh when she says that a contemporary home demands a contemporary form of cleaning.

At the end of the session she asks if I want to sleep with her.
The moment I am undressed I think that maybe this is not a good plan.
I proceed anyway.

FRIDAY 11 A.M. **XIANGMIN LU**

Lu asks me to explain Blixa Bargeld. Last week, on her request, I filled her iPod with my music and now one sentence from Bargeld is stuck in her head: "Ich bin das ganze chinesische Volk und Yü-Gung kann Berge versetzen, bin sechs Meter gross, bin neun Meter gross, bin zwölf Meter gross."

We listen to 'Yü-Gung' together and afterwards she says: "So this person says he is six meters tall, nine meters tall and so on, until the climax – that he is the entire population of China. Is it an arrogant fantasy or just deliberate hyperbole?" She grabs my hand while I walk her to the door. We end up under the shower.

TUESDAY 3 P.M. **MI FAN**

Fan still has troubles with the Feng Shui Master she hired. Her husband wants to fire him. I feel she is interested in something else.

"We are now discussing the Karaoke room. He says we should call it the 'recreation room', or even better the 'study room'. This morning we agreed it would be the 'library'.

I tell her that whatever the name of the space is, people shove a computer into it and sit around it at night.

Mi can be charming, and yet she seems to lack warmth. She arouses a feeling of unpleasantness in me. I am thinking about telling her not to come back anymore.

TUESDAY 5 P.M. **JU SHANGWEI**

"The whole trouble with the world today is that for all the talk about urbanization, our society is not organized on its principle."

THURSDAY 10 A.M. **NEI QIQI**

We continue our session on the city. Qiqi is making interesting points and says that as cities have expanded over the past decades, it has become harder and harder in metropolitan areas for a wealthy family to establish éliteness on the basis of family lineage. One result of this is the growing importance of going to a proper private school, restaurant, clubs and shopping malls. She gives me the Mercedes Benz R500 example and a list of courtyards she is looking to buy. In a moment of self-reflection she confesses that her buildings are worshiped in cities where she never considered building and despised in the cities where she worked in.

MONDAY 3 P.M. **XUFANG CHEN**

In-between our meetings Chen was asked to demolish a building.
"It is going to disappear, the decision is already taken, and to be honest, we all know the building didn't perform. Just the wrong type of architecture. Too much concrete, the people said. And you know what happens when the people start talking."

Now he asks me how to dismantle a high-rise, "but in such a way that I can make profit out of it."

I tell him that with historic buildings it is usually easier: "You collect the stones, window frames and wooden doors and ask an artist to make a new structure out of them. You exhibit that in some random European city."
I give Bordeaux, Košice, Mechlin and Plzen as examples. "This could work for new buildings as well."

For the large part of the session he is silent.

I tell him it isn't easy being an architect in these times of unbridled confusion, where one faces the loss of a stable architectural order and the need to deal with the promise of a better, freer and more individualized future.

TUESDAY 3 A.M. **HUA YU**

Yu complains continuously during the session and says to be constantly surrounded by people with the wrong eyewear.

"It just can happen all of a sudden. For example, last week I flew to Fuzhou. The plane took off, I fall asleep and upon waking up find myself surrounded by women wearing knock-off designer glasses. It's the logo you know, not the design. It can happen, and when it did, it scared the hell out of me."

She keeps on telling that the in-flight entertainment business is controlled by people who have not the slightest interest in culture, by people that are too stupid to think, but not too ashamed to make money during someone else's free time. The airplane is a tool to reinforce the stupidity that has engulfed the world, washed it away into a circumglobal digital debris of blockbusters, news coverage and pranks.

"It is all about candid camera on those airplanes, you think you escape them when you leave the earth and then you enter this masochistic Allen Funt Fantasy World. In there we are all prisoners of Punk'd. Scary shit!"

The airplane is a cultural crash happening in between two cities. It is in this momentary suspension, while cruising over continents, that a new culture could enfold. She says it is about rearranging time in order to alter life. Once you enter the airport, few choices are left.

Yu forgets her luggage in the office.

FRIDAY 8 P.M. MA MAHUHU

I tell Mahuhu that architecture is in a very problematic situation. Suddenly I quote Werner Herzog's 'in celluloid we trust' sentence from 'The White Diamond'. It has been stuck in my head ever since I saw it. I show him the fragment in which the director is lifting off from the earth in a blimp, ready to document the canopy of the rainforest and potentially being sucked down by a waterfall.

I freeze the frame on Herzog's face.

"No architect would ever proclaim 'in architecture we trust'. "

Maybe all of them would, he replies. And that is where Lu and I have a problem. Unrelated, I inform him that I am considering moving the office. All of my clients, with exception of Fei Fei, thought it was too far from the Central Business District. Mahuhu says the compound indeed looks old.

Then we have a discussion on why people despise the pre-Olympic building boom.

"After that nobody cared about the city anymore. That's a real advantage for architects. It offers more opportunities." ■

This contribution is based on, and uses samples of writing from, The Status Seekers by Vance Packard, Vance (Penguin Books, Middlesex, 1961).

BERT DE MUYNCK

SA
MAN
THA

by Douglas Coupland

'Value fictions' was a notion invented by designers Anthony Dunne and Fiona Raby in their 2001 book 'Design Noir: The Secret Life of Electronic Objects'. As opposed to scientific fictions, they used this device to embody unusual values into everyday objects hence producing a social critique of their respective contexts. Douglas Coupland's novels are invariably about value sets and how such value sets – or their absence – define a deviant social status quo, aspects of popular culture, and, occasionally, the traits of a whole cross-section of society. Thus, the term Generation X was made famous through Coupland's first novel in 1991, albeit after sociological findings which originally surfaced in the UK during the Sixties. If the notion became catchy and referential, Coupland's ulterior success as a storyteller derived, moreover, from an exquisite ability to blend cultural types and emerging techno-pop trends. In this vein he became an experimental writer of sorts, one whose language immediately reflects collective change, while depicting the contemporary urbanscape in an ironic and highly personal fashion. As Eleanor Rigby's Liz Dunn would tells us of a clinic in Vancouver, this would be "one of those buildings I've driven by a thousand times and never noticed, sort of like the architectural version of myself. Inside, it was cool and smelled of sanitation products." Ultimately, the following excerpt of Generation A not only illustrates the narrative structure of Coupland's latest novel – being one of the short-stories-cum-chapters through which the action makes its progress around the five main characters – but it also pays tribute to the magnificent description of Douglas Coupland's value fictions as "occupying the perplexing hinterland between optimism about the future and everyday apocalyptic paranoia." — P. G.

R ight.

When I was stung I was standing in a clump of grass beside a blossoming Ramayana shrub while a small flock of Barbary doves whistled over my
head. It felt like the old days, when blossoming shrubs and flowers were
something we could take for granted. My particular clump of grass was at
the corner of Weber Fork Road and Route 52, about as remote as it gets on
the island – twenty miles in from the east coast, in the hilly eastern part of
Wanganui province. Thing is, I'd taken a slice of boring white bread from its
bakery bag and had slapped it onto a small patch of yellow sandy dirt.
I was standing up to photograph the slice of bread using my mobile phone.
Why would you have been doing this? I hear you wonder. Excellent question. I was making an 'Earth sandwich'. What is an Earth sandwich? Fair
enough. It's when you use online maps to locate the exact opposite place
on the planet from you, and then hook up with some one close to that place.
Then, after you mathematically figure out exact opposite GPS coordinates
to within a thumb nail's radius, you put a slice of bread on that spot, then
connect via cellphone and simultaneously snap photos: two slices of bread
with a planet between them. It's an Internet thing. You make the sandwich,
you post it, and maybe someone somewhere will see it, and once they've
seen it, you've created art. Bingo.

The person on the other end of the earth was this girl, Simone Ferrero,
who was in central Madrid at the corner of Calle Gutenberg and Calle
Poeta Esteban de Villegas, at ten o'clock at night – meaning it was ten

o'clock in the morning in New Zealand. All I knew of her was that we had agreed online to make a sandwich together.

The thing is, New Zealanders pretty much have the Earth sandwich game locked up. Most of the planet's land masses are above the equator and are sandwich partners only with oceans. For example, the other side of North America's sandwich is entirely composed of the Indian Ocean. Honolulu makes a sliver of a sandwich with Zimbabwe, but that's all the opportunities there are for Yanks, Mexicans and Canadians. The thing is that even while I was taking my photo and being stung, my mind was somewhere else. I'd had a strange phone call that morning from my mother. It was my one sleep-in day of the week, but I'd foolishly forgotten to turn off my mobile phone. For the six other days a week I'm up at 5:00 a.m. to be at the gym to train clients for 6:00, and on my one day of rest I picked up the phone and …

"Samantha, good morning."

"Mum."

"Did I wake you up? It's 8:30. I thought for sure you'd be awake."

"Mum, what's up? Wait – I thought you were on vacation."

"We are. We're sixty minutes out of Darwin in a darling little cabin room, and at breakfast we had chocolate brioches and milk and – sorry, dear – I'm getting away from my message."

"What's your message?"

"I … we … your father and I, we have some news for you."

Yoinks. I braced myself for the worst, my brain already screaming for coffee.

"We've had a discussion, and we thought we should tell you something."

Cancer? Bankruptcy? Double yoinks. "What's wrong?"

"Your father and I have decided that we don't believe in anything any more."

"You what?"

"What I just said."

"Jesus, Mum, you phoned me up on a Monday morning to tell me you don't believe in anything."

"Yes."

"You mean, like, God? And religion?"

"Both."

I walked to the kitchen to flip the switch on the Braun. My parakeet, Timbo, a happy remnant of a failed relationship, was sitting on a deck chair, squawking the words "the worst toilet in Scotland" over and over and awaiting his morning treat. "Right. So why are you telling me this?"

"Well, I believe you still believe in things."

"What do you mean, things?"

"God. Life after death. That sort of thing."

"That sort of thing?" My sketchy belief system wasn't something to haggle about at this time of day, and my brain was racing ass over tit trying to figure out the significance of a call like this. I opened the window and threw Timbo an arrowroot biscuit. "So, Mum, what did you believe in before you stopped believing in things?" In the background the Braun was beginning to hiss, and I was glad that the absent bees hadn't wiped out the planet's coffee crop.

"Not much, really. But we've decided to make it official."

"This is pretty strange, Mum."

"No stranger than that afternoon you announced you were becoming a vegetarian."

"I was thirteen. It was either that or an eating disorder."

"Beliefs are beliefs."

"Crikey dick, Mum, but you don't believe in anything. You just said so. And I'm going to have to ask you a rude question, but are you on drugs?"

"Sam! No. We're only taking Solon. It's safe."

"Solon? That stuff that makes time pass quicker?"

"No. Solon is a lovely drug and it makes my head feel calm."

"Okay. It's still a drug."

My mother sighed, which was my cue to say something duti ful and reassuring, my role in the family as first-born. So I said, "It was thoughtful of you to call me and tell me properly."

"Thank you, dear. I don't know how your brothers will take it."

"They won't care. They don't think about this kind of stuff."

"You're right."

Thing is, my brothers are two fuckwits, and lately they'd been taxing my good will by hitting me up for loans and asking me to glue them back together after their neverending streams of failed relationships with the North Island's daggiest women. I poured myself a coffee and cut it with hot tap water. "So how do you think this is going to affect your life?"

"Probably not much. We're not going to proselytize – if people we know still choose to believe in something, we keep our mouths shut."

"That's it?"

"That's it."

"Right."

We hung up and I looked at my laptop clock. Making an Earth sandwich would take my mind off it all. I finished my coffee, showered, dressed and grabbed my asthma inhaler, and soon I was on my way to visit –40.4083°, 176.3204°.

The road eastward out of Palmy was empty.

And my conversation with Mum got me thinking about parents and how they feed your belief systems. I mean, whatever your parents do, good or bad, it allows you to do the same thing with no feelings of guilt. Dad steals cars? Go for it. Mum goes to church every Sunday? You better go too. So, when your parents decide they don't believe in anything, you can't rebel against them, because that'd just be rebelling against nothing. It puts you in a state of moral free float. If you copy them and believe in nothing yourself, then it's the same thing: copying nothing equals zero. You're buggered either way.

I wound around the rolling hills. What did I believe in? I'd had five different boyfriends in my twenty-six years, and the boot of each of their vehicles bore a different variation of the Christian fish. Coincidence?

First off, there was the tousle-haired Kevin, the catalogue model, who had an agape fish on his Honda. Kevin always seemed to have a religious reason for avoiding reality, most memorably not picking me up after work so he could shoot hoops with a Christian men's group. Relationship breaker. Then there was Miles, the Deadhead atheist, whose fish had DARWIN embedded in its interior. After him came Hal, whose silver fish was followed by the words "AND CHIPS." After Hal was Ray, who was a total wanker – I don't know what I was thinking when I was with him. Everyone has a Ray somewhere in his or her past. Ray's fish wasn't witty and ironic or anything – it was just a fish. And finally there was Reid, who had a chromed fish skeleton. I thought Reid was going to be the Keeper, but Reid was generic in his willingness to avoid commitment. Jesus, look at me labelling these guys like this. In all fairness, they'd probably label me a stuck-up gym bunny and claim that it wasn't their duty to provide me with their version of the fish like it was shade on a hot day.

So, yes, I had a few things on my mind when I was photographing my bread slice on a sheep-stinking roadside, not the least of which was jealousy about being in the other hemisphere – the loser's hemisphere – of being the opposite of Madrid, and sadness because the bees had vanished and therefore so many roadside flowers had all but vanished with them: the cudweed, the monkey musk, the brass buttons, the catchfly. I felt a generalized sense of wonder about the size of the planet and my useless little role atop it or under it. And then my cellphone rang and, as I said, I got stung.

Bingo. ∎

Extracted from 'Generation A' by Douglas Coupland. Published by William Heinemann.
© Douglas Coupland 2009.

BEYOND NO 3
TRENDS
AND FADS

Call for contributions

In 1905, Georg Simmel published 'The Philosophy of Fashion', a seminal text in which the German sociologist depicts with foretelling accuracy the quintessential psychological traits of the contemporary metropolitan character.

Nowadays, while the many happily embrace consumption as lifestyle and instantly embark in any fad that may fulfill a sense of permanent gratification, the very few that claim to resist the lure of fashion also constantly fail to understand and investigate the mechanisms by which trends and fads actually affect cultural productions at every level.

Architecture and urban creation do not escape a tendency that is pervasive in all cultural scopes, and which is the inescapable impact that both long-term trends and short-notice fads have on the production and consumption of ideas, objects and sites.

From celebrity to everyday culture, from gravity to ornament, from iconology to no-branding, from affluence to asceticism, from aestheticization to ugliness, from depression to optimism, from startecture to emergence, from pressure groups to particular interests, which are the currents and whims that are today deeply affecting the definition of our cityscapes?

www.sunarchitecture.nl/beyond